AS Maths Pocket Formu...

Geha

Contents

Pure 1

Algebra 1
Coordinate geometry 12
Series 13
Trigonometry 14
Differentiation 19
Integration 22

Pure 2

Algebra and functions 25
Trigonometry 32
Differentiation and integration . 39
Numerical methods 42

Note: The entire contents of Pure 1 and 2 apply to all exam boards unless otherwise stated.

Mechanics

Vectors 44
Kinematics 47
Statics 51
Dynamics 55

Statistics

Representing data 58
Probability 64
Discrete random variables ... 68
The normal distribution 72
Correlation and regression . 73

Note: For Mechanics and Statistics, the relevant components for each exam board have been indicated.

Decision Mathematics

Algorithms 75
Graphs and networks 77
Critical path analysis 86
Linear programming 88
Matchings 92

Note: The contents of Decision Mathematics apply only to AQA, Edexcel and OCR Mathematics exam boards. The relevant components for each of these three boards have been indicated.

Index 93

INTRODUCTION

This Mathematics Pocket Book was conceived after countless suggestions made by students for a comprehensive, easy-to-follow guide that covers all aspects of the syllabus. It covers the full course requirement of the following examination boards:

- AQA Mathematics
- Edexcel Mathematics
- OCR Mathematics
- WJEC Mathematics
- NICCEA Mathematics

This AS book gives students step-by-step methods to solve many maths problems, with valuable commentary and advice. It contains 'All You Need To Know', so any student with full knowledge of this pocket book should be well prepared for the AS exams.

Published by HarperCollins*Publishers* Limited
77–85 Fulham Palace Road
Hammersmith London W6 8JB
www.fireandwater.com

www.CollinsEducation.com
Online support for schools and colleges

© HarperCollins*Publishers* Limited 2002
First published 2002
Reprinted 10 9 8 7 6 5 4 3 2 1
ISBN 0 00 713413 4

Jeff Geha asserts the moral right to be identified as the author of this work.

All rights reserved. No part of this publication may be reproduced, stored in a retrieval system, or transmitted in any form or by any means, electronic, mechanical, photocopying, recording or otherwise, without either the prior permission of the Publisher or a licence permitting restricted copying in the United Kingdom issued by the Copyright Licensing Agency Ltd., 90 Tottenham Court Road, London W1P 0LP.

This book is sold subject to the condition that it shall not by way of trade or otherwise be lent, hired out or otherwise circulated without the Publisher's prior consent.

British Library Cataloguing in Publication Data
A Catalogue record for this publication is available from the British Library

Edited by Joan Miller
Designed by Merlin Group International and Ann Miller
Artwork by Merlin Group International and Ann Miller
Cover design by Susi Martin-Taylor
Printed in Great Britain by Martins the Printers Ltd, Berwick upon Tweed

PURE 1 — ALGEBRA

Index laws

Index laws are very important. You need to use them when simplifying algebraic expressions and solving equations.

Learn these laws in both the forward and reverse directions.

- $x^0 = 1$
- $x^{-a} = \dfrac{1}{x^a}$
- $\sqrt{x} = x^{\frac{1}{2}}$
- $(x^a)^b = x^{ab}$
- $\left(\dfrac{1}{x^a}\right)^b = x^{-ab}$
- $\left(\dfrac{a}{b}\right)^n = \dfrac{a^n}{b^n}$

- $\sqrt[n]{x} = x^{\frac{1}{n}}$
- $x^a \times x^b = x^{a+b}$
- $\dfrac{x^a}{x^b} = x^{a-b}$
- $x^{\frac{a}{b}} = (x^{\frac{1}{b}})^a = \sqrt[b]{x^a}$
- $(xy)^a = x^a \times y^a$
- $\left(\dfrac{a}{b}\right)^{\frac{1}{n}} = \dfrac{a^{\frac{1}{n}}}{b^{\frac{1}{n}}}$

Example

Solve for x: $3^{x+5} = 81$

Solution

$3^{x+5} = 3^4$ (as $81 = 3^4$)

$\therefore x + 5 = 4$

$x = {}^-1$

Surds

Surds are numerical expressions that include irrational numbers. You need to remember the following rules of surds.

- $\sqrt{a} \times \sqrt{a} = a$
- $\sqrt{a} \times \sqrt{b} = \sqrt{ab}$
- $a\sqrt{b} + c\sqrt{b} = (a+c)\sqrt{b}$
- $a\sqrt{b} \times c\sqrt{b} = ac\sqrt{b^2} = acb$
- $\sqrt{a^2 b} = \sqrt{a^2} \times \sqrt{b^2} = a\sqrt{b}$

Rationalising the denominator

If the denominator of a fraction includes a surd, you can **rationalise** it. If the denominator is a single surd, multiply the top and bottom by the same surd. If the denominator has more than one term, multiply top and bottom by its **conjugate**.

Note: $(\sqrt{a} + \sqrt{b})$ and $(\sqrt{a} - \sqrt{b})$ are conjugates.

Multiplying a surd by its conjugate always gives a whole number.

$$(\sqrt{a} + \sqrt{b})(\sqrt{a} - \sqrt{b}) = \sqrt{a^2} - \sqrt{ab} + \sqrt{ab} - \sqrt{b^2}$$
$$= a - b$$

Useful hints for rationalising the denominator

If the surd is in the form:

- $\dfrac{1}{\sqrt{a}}$ multiply by $\dfrac{\sqrt{a}}{\sqrt{a}}$

- $\dfrac{1}{\sqrt{a} - \sqrt{b}}$ multiply by $\dfrac{\sqrt{a} + \sqrt{b}}{\sqrt{a} + \sqrt{b}}$

- $\dfrac{1}{a + \sqrt{b}}$ multiply by $\dfrac{a - \sqrt{b}}{a - \sqrt{b}}$

Functions

One-one function

A function $y = f(x)$ is a **one-one function** if it passes the horizontal line test (i.e. any horizontal line cuts the graph at no more than one point).

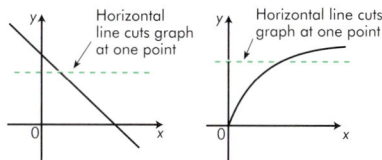

Many-one function

If a horizontal line cuts the curve in more than one point then $y = f(x)$ is **many-one**.

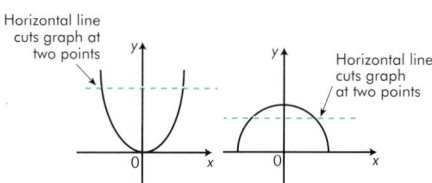

Note: A relation is said to be a function if a vertical line cuts the graph at no more than one point.

Domain and range

For $y = f(x)$, the domain is the set of all possible x-values and the range is all possible y-values.

Here is a summary of the domain and range of some common functions.

Parabola

$y = x^2 + a$

Domain: all real x

Range: $y \geq a$

Hyperbola $y = \dfrac{a}{x + b}$

Domain = all real x, $x \neq {}^-b$

Range: all real y, $y \neq 0$

Semicircle

$y = \sqrt{a^2 - x^2}$

Domain: ${}^-a \leq x \leq a$

Range: $0 \leq y \leq a$

Exponential curve

$y = a^x$

Domain: all real x

Range: $y > 0$

PURE 1 — ALGEBRA

Circle

$(x - a)^2 + (y - b)^2 = r^2$

centre (a, b), radius $= r$

Domain: $a - r \leq x \leq a + r$

Range: $b - r \leq y \leq b + r$

Square root

$y = \sqrt{ax + b}$

Domain: $x \geq -\dfrac{b}{a}$

Range: $y \geq 0$

Quadratic expansions/factorisations

The general equation $y = ax^2 + bx + c$ where $a \neq 0$ is called a **quadratic equation**. Make sure you know the following quadratic expansions and **factorisations**.

- $(a + b)^2 = a^2 + 2ab + b^2$
- $(a - b)^2 = a^2 - 2ab + b^2$
- $(a - b)(a + b) = a^2 - b^2$
- $(x + a)(x + b) = x^2 + (a + b)x + ab$

Quadratic equations

Rule: If $a \times b = 0$, then $a = 0$ or $b = 0$ or both.
When solving quadratic equations:

- Check to see if the equation can be **factorised**.
- If yes, then it can be solved using the above rule.
- If not, then the solution to the quadratic equation $ax^2 + bx + c = 0$ is given by:

$$x = \frac{-b \pm \sqrt{b^2 - 4ac}}{2a} \qquad \textbf{(Quadratic formula)}$$

The discriminant

The quadratic formula gives the roots of $ax^2 + bx + c = 0$ as:

$$x = \frac{-b \pm \sqrt{b^2 - 4ac}}{2a}$$

The expression $b^2 - 4ac$ is called the **discriminant** and its value is denoted by Δ (delta). The discriminant reveals the number of solutions (i.e. roots).

- Real roots $\qquad\qquad\qquad\qquad \Delta \geq 0$
- Two real roots $\qquad\qquad\qquad \Delta > 0$
- Exactly one root/repeated root $\quad \Delta = 0$
- No real roots $\qquad\qquad\qquad\quad \Delta < 0$

Example

For what values of m does the equation $3x^2 - mx + 12 = 0$ have a repeated root?

Solution

$\Delta = b^2 - 4ac = (^-m)^2 - 4 \times 3 \times 12 = m^2 - 144$

For one root $\Delta = 0$ so $m^2 - 144 = 0$
$$m^2 = 144$$
$$m = \pm 12$$

Quadratic graphs

The graph of $y = ax^2 + bx + c$ is a parabola. Follow these steps to sketch the curve.

Step 1: Find the roots of the equation, either by **factorisation** or the quadratic formula.

Step 2: Find the coordinates of the vertex. Its x-coordinate is midway between the roots.

Step 3: Find the coordinates of the y-intercept (i.e. at $x = 0$).

Step 4: Sketch the curve. Note that if $a > 0$ the parabola is **concave up** and if $a < 0$ the parabola is **concave down**.

Notes:
- If the parabola has no real roots (from step 1), you find the coordinates of the vertex by completing the square.
- A much simpler method that can be used for sketching parabolas is covered later in this section.

Completing the square

Completing the square involves expressing quadratic equations as perfect squares.

Use the fact that $x^2 + 2bx = (x + b)^2 - b^2$.

Follow these steps to complete the square for $ax^2 + bx + c = 0$.

Step 1: Divide the quadratic equation by the coefficient of x^2, as the coefficient of x^2 must always be 1.

$$x^2 + \frac{b}{a}x + \frac{c}{a} = 0$$

Step 2: Form the perfect square by halving the coefficient of x to find the constant term inside the brackets.

$$(x + \frac{b}{2a})^2 + \ldots = 0$$

Step 3: Subtract $(\frac{b}{2a})^2$ to form the perfect square.

$$(x + \frac{b}{2a})^2 - (\frac{b}{2a})^2 + \frac{c}{a} = 0 \text{ or } (x + \frac{b}{2a})^2 = (\frac{b}{2a})^2 - \frac{c}{a}$$

Example

By completing the square, find the coordinates of the vertex of the curve $y = x^2 + 4x + 9$.

Solution

Step 1: Coefficient of x^2 is 1 so there is no need to divide.

Step 2: Half the coefficient of x is 2. The 'squared' term is $(x + 2)^2$.

Step 3: Subtract $2^2 = 4$

$$\therefore y = x^2 + 4x + 9$$
$$= (x + 2)^2 - 4 + 9$$
$$= (x + 2)^2 + 5$$

As $(x + 2)^2 > 0$, the vertex of the curve (a minimum) is at the point with coordinates $(^-2, 5)$.

Pure 1 — Algebra

Sketching other functions

When you sketch graphs of other functions, you are expected first to find the points where the curve intersects the coordinate axes (i.e. axial intercepts) and then to fit the curve through these points, using what you know about the basic curve.

You need to be familiar with the basic graphs of the following relations.

Cubics

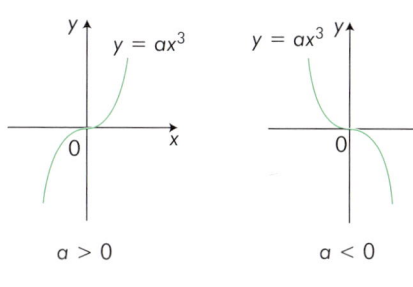

Note: For higher powers of x (e.g. $y = ax^5$, $y = ax^7$) the graphs look similar but they are flatter between x-values of $^-1$ and 1 and steeper elsewhere.

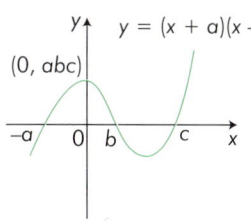

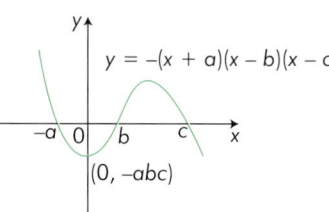

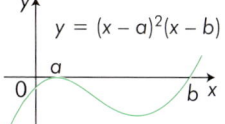

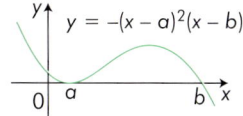

Quartics

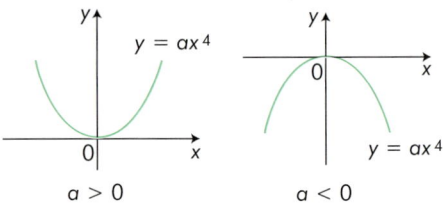

Note: For higher powers of x (e.g. $y = ax^6$, $y = ax^8$) the graphs look similar but they are flatter between x-values of $^-1$ and 1 and steeper elsewhere.

Hyperbolas

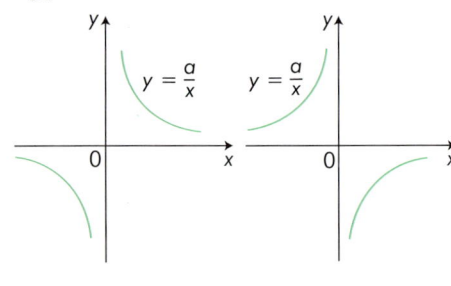

Note: For higher powers of x (e.g. $y = \dfrac{a}{x^3}$, $y = \dfrac{a}{x^5}$) the graphs look similar but are steeper between x-values of $^-1$ and 1 and flatter elsewhere.

Note: For higher powers of x (e.g. $y = \dfrac{a}{x^4}$, $y = \dfrac{a}{x^6}$) the graphs look similar but are steeper between x-values of $^-1$ and 1 and flatter elsewhere.

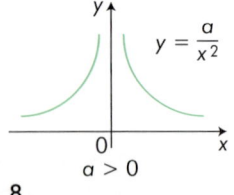
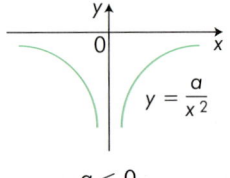

Modulus function

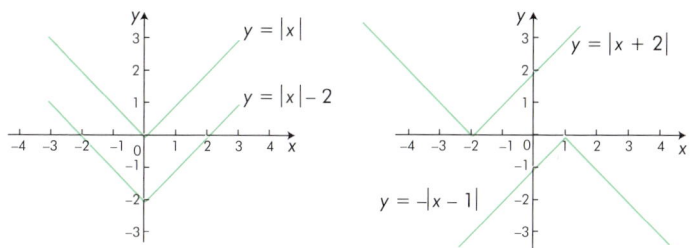

Graphical transformations

You also need to be able to perform simple transformations to the basic curves covered earlier.

Consider the basic curve $y = f(x)$.

New function	Transformation
$y = f(x) + c$	The basic curve is shifted c units **up** (if $c > 0$) or **down** (if $c < 0$).
$y = f(x - b)$	The basic curve is shifted b units **right** (if $b > 0$) or **left** (if $b < 0$).
$y = af(x)$	For $a > 1$, the basic curve is **stretched up** and for $0 < a < 1$ the curve is **compressed down** by a factor of a in the **y-direction**.
	For $a = {}^-1$, the basic curve is reflected in the x-axis.
$y = f(ax)$	For $a > 1$, the basic curve is **compressed inwards** and for $0 < a < 1$ the curve is **stretched outwards** by a factor of a in the x-direction.
	For $a = {}^-1$, the basic curve is **reflected** in the y-axis.

Simultaneous equations

There are two methods of solving these.

- **Elimination:** Make the coefficients of one unknown the same in both equations, then add or subtract the equations to eliminate that unknown.
- **Substitution:** Make one of the unknowns the subject in one equation and substitute into the other equation.

With either method, you must obtain the value for each unknown. Check your result by direct substitution in the original equation. If one of the equations is a quadratic, use the substitution method.

Quadratic identities

If $a_1x^2 + b_1x + c_1 = a_2x^2 + b_2x + c_2$ for more than two values of x, then $a_1 = a_2$, $b_1 = b_2$, $c_1 = c_2$.
The above theorem also applies to polynomials of higher powers.

Polynomials

The general form of the polynomial P(x) is given by:

$P(x) = a_nx^n + a_{n-1}x^{n-1} + \ldots + a_1x + a_0$

Features of the polynomial P(x)

- $a_0, a_1, \ldots, a_n$ are coefficients.
- a_n is the **leading coefficient**.
- a_nx^n is the **leading term**.
- P(x) is of degree n. The degree is the highest power.
- A number a is a **zero** of P(x) if P(a) = 0. It is also called a **root** or **solution** of P(x) = 0. The graph of P(x) cuts the x-axis at $x = a$.
- A polynomial of degree n cannot have more than n distinct zeros.

The factor theorem

If P(a) = 0, then $(x - a)$ is a factor of P(x).

Inequalities

Linear inequalities

When solving linear inequalities, you need to know that:

- the inequality sign is unchanged if the inequality is multiplied or divided by a positive number

- the inequality sign is unchanged if you add or subtract the same positive or negative number to both sides

- the inequality sign is reversed if the inequality is multiplied or divided by a negative number.

Example

Solve: $3 - 2x \geq 5$.

Solution

$3 - 2x \geq 5$
$ - 2x \geq 2$ (subtracting 3 from both sides)
$ x \leq {}^-1$ (dividing both sides by $^-2$)

Quadratic inequalities

These problems are best solved graphically.

Example

Solve: $5x - 2 - 2x^2 > 0$.

Solution

Let $y = 5x - 2 - 2x^2$
$ = -(2x^2 - 5x + 2)$
$ = -(2x - 1)(x - 2)$

Now sketch this parabola.

Note that this parabola is concave down with roots at $x = 0.5, 2$.

From the graph, $y > 0$ when $0.5 < x < 2$.

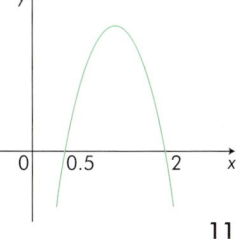

Equation of a straight line

Equations of straight lines may be expressed in two forms.

- **Standard form**

  $ax + by + c = 0$ where a, b, c are integers.

- **Gradient-intercept form**

  $y = mx + b$ where m is the gradient and b is the y-intercept.

The gradient formula

The gradient, m, of a line joining two points $A(x_1, y_1)$ and $B(x_2, y_2)$:

$$m = \frac{y_2 - y_1}{x_2 - x_1}$$

The point gradient formula

The equation of a line through a point $A(x_1, y_1)$ with gradient m:

$$(y - y_1) = m(x - x_1)$$

The midpoint formula

The midpoint M, of the line segment joining $A(x_1, y_1)$ to $B(x_2, y_2)$:

$$M(x, y) = \left(\frac{x_1 + x_2}{2}, \frac{y_1 + y_2}{2} \right)$$

Parallel and perpendicular lines

Two lines with gradients m_1 and m_2 respectively are:

- parallel if $m_1 = m_2$
- perpendicular if $m_1 m_2 = {}^-1$

  i.e. $m_2 = -\left(\frac{1}{m_1} \right)$.

Arithmetic series

In an arithmetic progression (AP) the difference, d, between successive terms is constant. If u_1, u_2 and u_3 are the first three terms of an AP, then $u_2 - u_1 = u_3 - u_2 = d$.

To find the nth term, u_n, of an AP with common difference d, and first term a, use $u_n = a + (n-1)d$.

The sum to n terms, of an AP, $S_n = \frac{n}{2}[2a + (n-1)d]$ or $S_n = \frac{n}{2}[a + l]$ where l = last term.

The second formula can only be used if the last term, l, is known.

You may be given details about the sum to n terms, S_n, and the sum to $(n-1)$ terms, S_{n-1}, and asked to find u_n. In this case, use:

$S_n - S_{n-1} = u_n$

Geometric series

In a geometric progression (GP) the ratio, r, between successive terms is constant. If u_1, u_2 and u_3 are the first three terms in a GP:

$$\frac{u_2}{u_1} = \frac{u_3}{u_2} = r$$

The nth term, with common ratio r and first term a, is $u_n = ar^{n-1}$.

To find S_n, the sum to n terms, of a geometric series, use:

$$S_n = \frac{a(r^n - 1)}{r - 1} \text{ for } |r| > 1 \text{ i.e. } r > 1, r < {}^-1$$

or $S_n = \frac{a(1 - r^n)}{1 - r}$ for $|r| < 1$ i.e. ${}^-1 < r < 1$

Infinite geometric series

If ${}^-1 < r < 1$, then the sum of the GP converges and has a **limiting sum** (i.e. it tends towards some finite number as n tends to infinity).

If ${}^-1 < r < 1$, then $S_\infty = \frac{a}{1 - r}$ and S_∞ is the limiting sum.

PURE 1 — TRIGONOMETRY

Graphs of trigonometric functions

You need to be able to sketch the graphs of the **sine**, **cosine** and **tangent** functions and to know their special properties.

The graphs of trigonometric functions are periodic, i.e., the basic shape is repeated after a given interval called the **period**.

The **amplitude** is always measured as the distance from the middle value to the maximum value of the range (i.e. from the x-axis to the maximum y-value).

When you are sketching these functions, start by setting up a table of values. When you have drawn one period, you can repeat it to continue the curve.

$y = \sin x$

Period = 360° and amplitude = 1.

x	0°	90°	180°	270°	360°
sin x	0	1	0	⁻1	0

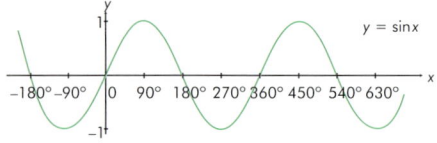

$y = \cos x$

Period = 360° and amplitude = 1.

x	0°	90°	180°	270°	360°
cos x	1	0	⁻1	0	1

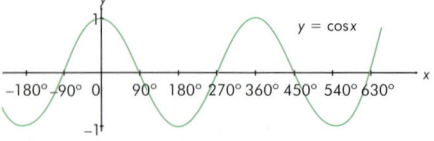

$y = \tan x$

Period = 180° and amplitude is undefined.

x	⁻90°	0°	90°	180°	270°
$\tan x$	undefined	0	undefined	0	undefined

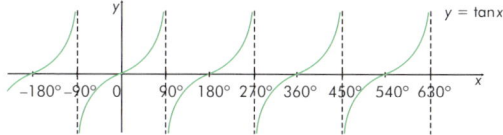

Sketching more difficult trigonometric functions

Exam boards commonly ask for sketches of trigonometric functions that are slight variations on the basic theme. This can best be approached by setting up a table of values at the critical points or by applying transformations to one of the basic graphs.

Example

Sketch the graph of $y = 1 + 3\sin 2x$, $0 < x < 360°$.

Solution

$y = 1 + 3\sin 2x$ Set up a table of values at the critical points.

i.e. $2x = 0°, 90°, 180°, 270°, 360°$ so $x = 0°, 45°, 90°, 135°, 180°$

x	0°	45°	90°	135°	180°
$1 + 3\sin 2x$	1	4	1	⁻2	1

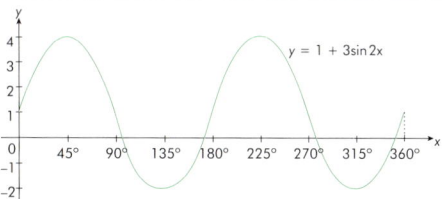

By transformation

The original curve $y = \sin x$ has been:

- **compressed** in by a factor 2 in the *x*-direction ($\sin 2x$)
- **stretched upwards** by a factor of 3 in the *y*-direction ($3 \sin 2x$) (Note that this means the amplitude is 3.)
- **shifted upwards** 1 unit ($1 + 3 \sin 2x$).

Exact ratios

The sine, cosine and tangent of 30°, 45° and 60° may be expressed exactly. The results are based on **Pythagoras' theorem**.

x	30°	45°	60°
$\sin x$	$\frac{1}{2}$	$\frac{1}{\sqrt{2}}$	$\frac{\sqrt{3}}{2}$
$\cos x$	$\frac{\sqrt{3}}{2}$	$\frac{1}{\sqrt{2}}$	$\frac{1}{2}$
$\tan x$	$\frac{1}{\sqrt{3}}$	1	$\sqrt{3}$

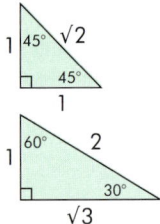

These ratios are often used in solving trigonometric equations.

Sign of circular functions

The sign of the functions sin, cos and tan for the four quadrants can be remembered by the mnemonic **ASTC** – 'All Stations To Central'.

All ratios positive in the 1st quadrant.
Sin only positive in the 2nd quadrant.
Tan only positive in the 3rd quadrant.
Cos only positive in the 4th quadrant.

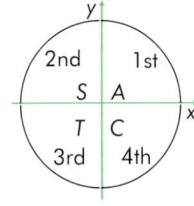

When solving trigonometric equations it's the 'criss-cross' angles that are most relevant (shown as θ between the bold lines and the horizontal axis).

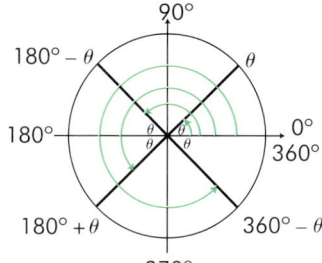

Noting that all angles are measured anticlockwise from the positive x-axis, the **positive solutions** for the various trigonometric identities are as follows:

- for **sin**: θ and $180° - \theta$
- for **cos**: θ and $360° - \theta$
- for **tan**: θ and $180° + \theta$

Equally, the **negative solutions** for the various trigonometric identities are as follows:

- for **sin**: $180° + \theta$, $360° - \theta$
- for **cos**: $180° - \theta$, $180° + \theta$
- for **tan**: $180° - \theta$, $360° - \theta$

These results are also true when angles are expressed in radians.

Identities and equations

The identities:

- $\tan x = \dfrac{\sin x}{\cos x}$
- $\sin^2 x + \cos^2 x = 1$

are very important for simplifying expressions and solving equations.

Example

Solve: $2\sin x = \cos x$ for $0 < x < 360°$.

Solution

$2 \sin x = \cos x$

$\dfrac{\sin x}{\cos x} = \dfrac{1}{2} \Rightarrow \tan x = 0.5$ (tan is +ve in the 1st and 3rd quadrants)

$\therefore x = 26.6°, (180° + 26.6°) = 26.6°, 206.6°$

Example

Prove that: $\dfrac{\sin \theta}{1 + \cos \theta} + \dfrac{\sin \theta}{1 - \cos \theta} = \dfrac{2}{\sin \theta}$.

Solution

$$\text{LHS} = \dfrac{\sin \theta}{1 + \cos \theta} + \dfrac{\sin \theta}{1 - \cos \theta}$$

$$= \dfrac{\sin \theta(1 - \cos \theta) + \sin \theta(1 + \cos \theta)}{(1 + \cos \theta)(1 - \cos \theta)}$$

$$= \dfrac{\sin \theta - \sin \theta \cos \theta + \sin \theta + \sin \theta \cos \theta}{1 - \cos^2 \theta}$$

$$= \dfrac{2 \sin \theta}{\sin^2 \theta}$$

$$= \dfrac{2}{\sin \theta} = \text{RHS}$$

Radians

Angles may also be measured in **radians**. A radian is the angle subtended at the centre of a circle by an arc of length equal to the radius of the circle.

You must be able to convert between radians and degrees. Noting that π radians = $180°$, to convert:

- from radians to degrees: multiply by $\dfrac{180°}{\pi}$

- from degrees to radians: multiply by $\dfrac{\pi}{180°}$.

PURE 1 — DIFFERENTIATION

Basic differentiation rules

Notation:	$\dfrac{dy}{dx}$, $f'(x)$, $\dfrac{d}{dx}(f(x))$, y'
Power rule:	$\dfrac{d}{dx}(x^n) = nx^{n-1}$, $\dfrac{d}{dx}(x^{-n}) = {}^-nx^{-n-1}$
Constant multiple rule:	$\dfrac{d}{dx}(cx^n) = cnx^{n-1}$, $\dfrac{d}{dx}(cx^{-n}) = {}^-cnx^{-n-1}$
Constant rule:	$\dfrac{d}{dx}(c) = 0$ (where c is a constant)
Sum/difference rule:	$\dfrac{d}{dx}[f(x) \pm g(x)] = f'(x) \pm g'(x)$

Tangents and normals to a curve

Edexcel, OCR, NICCEA

Follow these steps to find the equation of the tangent or normal to a curve at a point, say $x = x_1$.

Step 1: Find $f'(x)$.

Step 2: Substitute $x = x_1$ into $f'(x)$ to find the gradient of the tangent (m_t), i.e. $m_t = f'(x_1)$.

To find the gradient of normal (m_n) use $m_n = -\dfrac{1}{m_t}$.

Step 3: Find the equation of the tangent or normal by using the point-gradient formula $(y - y_1) = m(x - x_1)$.

Find y_1 by substituting $x = x_1$ into the original curve $y = f(x)$.

Increasing and decreasing functions

Use the derivative to find if a function is increasing or decreasing:

- If $\dfrac{dy}{dx} > 0$, the function is **increasing**.

- If $\dfrac{dy}{dx} < 0$, the function is **decreasing**.

Finding and identifying stationary points

Step 1: Find f'(x).

Step 2: Solve f'(x) = 0 for all values of x to determine the stationary points.

Step 3: Stationary points may be:
- maximum turning points
- minimum turning points
- stationary points of inflexion.

You can determine the nature of the stationary points as follows.

- If f'(x) < 0 to the left of a stationary point and f'(x) > 0 to the right of that point, then the stationary point is a **minimum**.

f'(x) < 0   f'(x) > 0

- If f'(x) > 0 to the left of a stationary point and f'(x) < 0 to the right of that point, then the stationary point is a **maximum**.

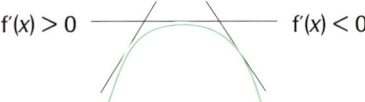

f'(x) > 0   f'(x) < 0

- If f'(x) has the same negative or positive sign on both sides of a stationary point, then the point is a **stationary point of inflexion**.

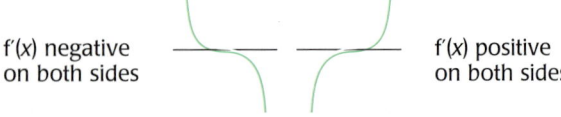

f'(x) negative   f'(x) positive
on both sides   on both sides

Curve sketching

To sketch a curve:

- find and identify the nature of the stationary points as described above
- find the point(s) at which the curve cuts the y-axis (i.e. $x = 0$) and x-axis (i.e. $y = 0$)
- find the equation of any asymptotes
- sketch the curve, indicating all the above features.

Maximum and minimum problems

Use the following steps to solve maximum and minimum problems.

Step 1: Express the problem algebraically – two expressions are generally required.

Step 2: Express the quantity, Q, to be **optimised** as a function of a single variable – keep the required expression in mind so that you know which variable needs to be eliminated.

Step 3: Differentiate Q and set the differential equal to zero to find the value of the independent variable at which Q is **optimised**.

Step 4: Verify that your answer yields the maximum or minimum by checking the sign of the derivative on either side of that point.

Indefinite integration

Integration is the reverse of differentiation. Below is a summary of the rules that relate to indefinite integrals.

Basic rules

Constant rule: $\qquad \int k \, dx = kx + c$

Power rule: $\qquad \int x^n \, dx = \dfrac{x^{n+1}}{n+1} + c, \ n \neq {}^{-}1$

Constant multiple rule: $\int k f(x) \, dx = k \int f(x) \, dx$

$$\int k x^n \, dx = k \int x^n \, dx = \dfrac{k x^{n+1}}{n+1} + c, n \neq {}^{-}1$$

Sum/difference rule: $\quad \int (f(x) \pm g(x)) \, dx = \int f(x) \, dx \pm \int g(x) \, dx$

Integrating $(ax + b)^n$: $\quad \int (ax+b)^n \, dx = \dfrac{(ax+b)^{n+1}}{a(n+1)} + c, n \neq {}^{-}1$

Definite integrals

In a definite integral you are given limits that are used to find its numerical value.

> If f(x) is a continuous function for $a < x < b$ and F(x) is the integral of f(x), then:
> $\int_a^b f(x) \, dx = \Big[F(x) \Big]_a^b = F(b) - F(a)$

Pure 1 — Integration

Properties of definite integrals

Below is a summary of some basic rules that relate to definite integrals.

- $\int_a^b f(x)\,dx = -\int_b^a f(x)\,dx$
- $\int_a^b k f(x)\,dx = k\int_a^b f(x)\,dx$
- $\int_a^b (f(x) \pm g(x))\,dx = \int_a^b f(x)\,dx \pm \int_a^b g(x)\,dx$
- $\int_a^b f(x)\,dx = \int_a^c f(x)\,dx + \int_c^b f(x)\,dx$, where $a < c < b$

Areas by integration

Exact area between a curve and the x-axis

Integration can be used to find the exact area between the curve $y = f(x)$ and the x-axis.

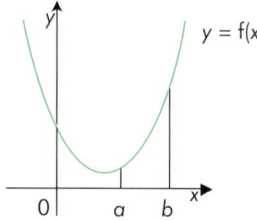

$A = \int_a^b f(x)\,dx = \left[F(x)\right]_a^b = F(b) - F(a)$

One important note to make here is that areas below the *x*-axis are always negative. In these circumstances you should always find the **absolute value** of each area.

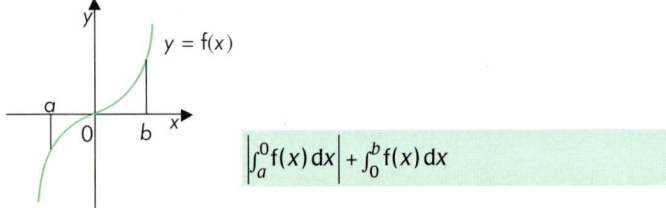

$$\left| \int_a^0 f(x)\,dx \right| + \int_0^b f(x)\,dx$$

Exact area between a curve and the *y*-axis
OCR, NICCEA

Similarly, integration can be used to find the exact area between the curve $x = g(y)$ and the *y*-axis.

The first essential step is to rearrange the function to obtain x in terms of y. The integral limits must be read off the *y*-axis.

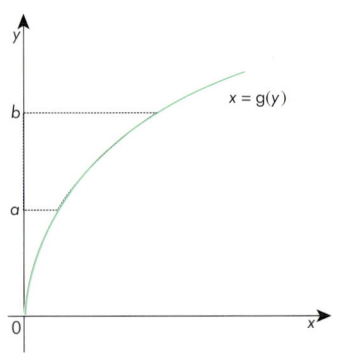

$$A = \int_a^b g(y)\,dy = \Big[G(y)\Big]_a^b = G(b) - G(a)$$

Pure 2 — Algebra and Functions

Inverse functions

A function $y = f(x)$ has an inverse function $f^{-1}(x)$, if a horizontal line intersects it in at most only one point.

Where the horizontal line intersects the curve in more than one point, then the function will only have an inverse if the domain is suitably restricted.

Finding the inverse function

The step-by-step method below explains how to find the inverse function of $y = f(x)$.

Step 1: Interchange x and y in $y = f(x)$.

Step 2: Rearrange the equation to give y in terms of x. This is the inverse function and is denoted by $f^{-1}(x)$.

Important features of $f^{-1}(x)$

There are two important features of $f^{-1}(x)$ in relation to $y = f(x)$.

- The **domain** of $f^{-1}(x)$ is the **range** of $y = f(x)$.
- The **range** of $f^{-1}(x)$ is the **domain** of $y = f(x)$.

The graph of $f^{-1}(x)$ is the reflection of the curve $y = f(x)$ in the line $y = x$.

Example

A function is defined by $f(x) = \dfrac{x^2}{x^2 - 4}$, $x > 0$, $x \neq \pm 2$.

Find the inverse function $f^{-1}(x)$ and hence state its domain and range.

Solution

Step 1: $y = \dfrac{x^2}{x^2 - 4}$, $x > 0$, $x \neq \pm 2$

interchanging x and y gives: $x = \dfrac{y^2}{y^2 - 4}$

Step 2: $x = \dfrac{y^2}{y^2 - 4}$

$xy^2 - 4x = y^2$

$y^2(x - 1) = 4x$

$y^2 = \dfrac{4x}{x - 1}$

$\therefore y = \pm \sqrt{\dfrac{4x}{x - 1}}$

i.e. $f^{-1}(x) = \pm \dfrac{2\sqrt{x}}{\sqrt{x - 1}}$

Since $x > 0$ for f(x), then $y > 0$ for $f^{-1}(x)$.

$\therefore f^{-1}(x) = \dfrac{2\sqrt{x}}{\sqrt{x - 1}}$

The domain of $f^{-1}(x)$ is the range of f(x)

i.e. $x > 1$.

The range of $f^{-1}(x)$ is the domain of f(x)

i.e. $y > 0$.

The modulus function

The graph of $y = |f(x)|$

The graph of $y = |f(x)|$ is the same as the graph of $y = f(x)$ but with the negative part of the curve reflected in the x-axis.

The graph of $y = f(|x|)$

The graph of $y = f(|x|)$ is the same as the graph of $y = f(x)$ when x is positive. This part of the graph is then reflected in the y-axis to give the graph of $y = f(|x|)$ for negative values of x.

Note: Graphs of typical modulus functions are shown on page 9.

PURE 2 — ALGEBRA AND FUNCTIONS

Binomial expansion
Edexcel, OCR, WJEC, NICCEA

For any positive integer n, the expansion of an expression of the form $(a + b)^n$ is called a **binomial expansion**.

$(a + b)^n = {_nC_0}a^n + {_nC_1}a^{n-1}b + \ldots + {_nC_n}b^n$

where: ${_nC_r} = \dfrac{n!}{r!(n-r)!}$

Note: Terms equidistant from the ends are equal.

${_nC_0} = {_nC_n} = 1$, ${_nC_1} = {_nC_{n-1}} = n$

and, in general, ${_nC_r} = {_nC_{n-r}}$

Polynomials
Edexcel, OCR, WJEC, NICCEA

Long division of polynomials

Long division of polynomials is similar to long division in numerical arithmetic.

Example
Divide $6x^3 - 5x^2 - 2x + 1$ by $(x - 1)$.

Solution

$$
\begin{array}{r}
6x^2 + x - 1 \\
(x-1)\overline{)\,6x^3 - 5x^2 - 2x + 1} \\
\underline{6x^3 - 6x^2} \\
x^2 - 2x \\
\underline{x^2 - x} \\
-x + 1 \\
\underline{-x + 1} \\
0
\end{array}
$$

$6x^3 - 5x^2 - 2x + 1 = (x - 1)(6x^2 + x - 1)$
$ = (x - 1)(3x - 1)(2x + 1)$

The remainder theorem
OCR, WJEC, NICCEA

If a polynomial P(x) is divided by $(x - a)$, the remainder R is found by calculating $P(a)$.

Example

Find the remainder when the polynomial $P(x) = x^3 - 2x^2 + 5$ is divided by $(x + 1)$.

Solution

The remainder R is given by $P(a)$ for $a = {}^-1$.

$P(^-1) = (^-1)^3 - 2(^-1)^2 + 5$
$ = {}^-1 - 2 + 5$
$ = 2$

Exponential functions

The exponential function is represented by e^x where e is an irrational number (like π or $\sqrt{2}$) and has an approximate value of 2.718.

Graph of $y = e^x$

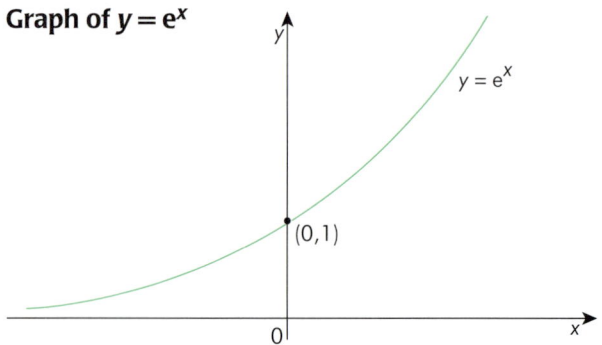

Properties of $y = e^x$

- The graph passes through (0, 1).
- $e^x > 0$ for all x.
- It is always increasing.
- Asymptote: x-axis.
- As $x \to \infty$, $e^x \to \infty$.
- As $x \to {}^-\infty$, $e^x \to 0$.

Graphs of other exponential functions

You need to be able to sketch graphs with slight variations on the basic curve $y = e^x$.

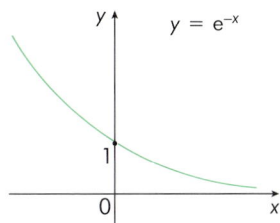

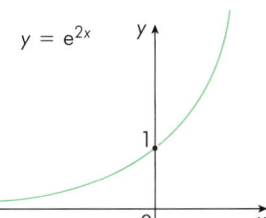

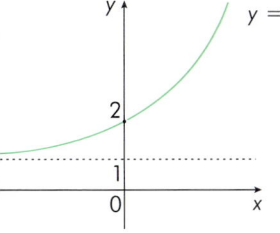

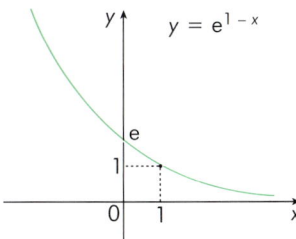

Logarithmic functions

Logarithms to the base e are called **natural logarithms**. They are the ones you are most concerned with in this topic.

The natural logarithmic function is represented by $\log_e x$ or simply by $\ln x$.

Graph of $y = \log_e x$

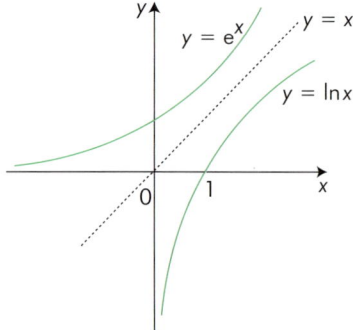

Properties of $y = \log_e x$

- The graph passes through (1, 0).
- It is only defined for $x > 0$.
- It is always increasing.
- Asymptote: y-axis.
- As $x \to \infty$, $\ln x \to \infty$.
- As $x \to 0$, $\ln x \to {}^-\infty$.

Graphs of other logarithmic functions

Again you need to be able to sketch graphs with slight variations on the basic curve $y = \ln x$.

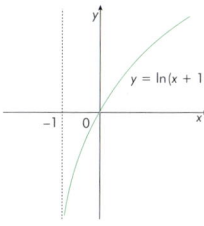

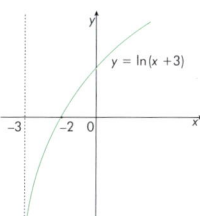

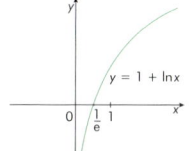

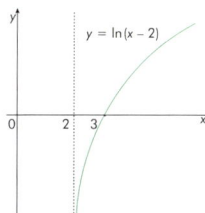

Logarithmic laws

You need to know the logarithmic laws.

- $\log_a a = 1$
- $\log_a 1 = 0$
- $\log_a (mn) = \log_a m + \log_a n$
- $\log_a \dfrac{m}{n} = \log_a m - \log_a n$
- $\log_a (m^n) = n \log_a m$
- $\log_a b = \dfrac{\log_c b}{\log_c a}$

Secant, cosecant and cotangent

Edexcel, NICCEA

$y = \operatorname{cosec} x = \dfrac{1}{\sin x}$ Period = 2π, no amplitude

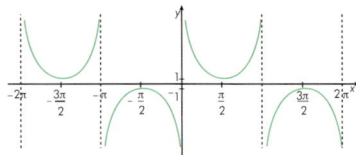

$y = \sec x = \dfrac{1}{\cos x}$ Period = 2π, no amplitude

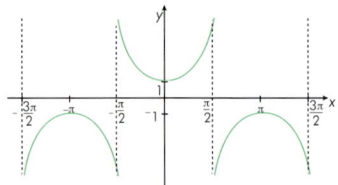

$y = \cot x = \dfrac{1}{\tan x} = \dfrac{\cos x}{\sin x}$ Period = 2π, no amplitude

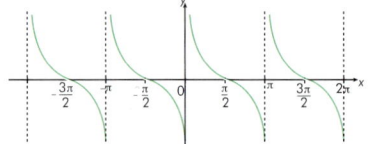

Inverse trigonometric functions
Edexcel

The sine, cosine and tangent functions are many-one so they do not have inverses over their full domains. However, it is possible to restrict their domains so that each one has an inverse.

The graphs of these inverse functions are given below.

$y = \sin^{-1} x$

Domain: $-1 \leq x \leq 1$

Range: $-\dfrac{\pi}{2} \leq y \leq \dfrac{\pi}{2}$

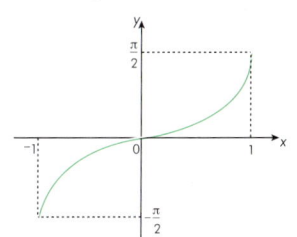

$y = \cos^{-1} x$

Domain: $-1 \leq x \leq 1$

Range: $0 \leq y \leq \pi$

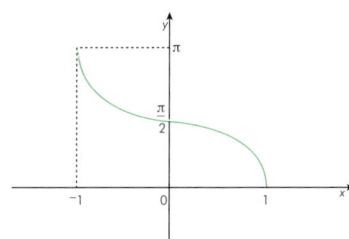

$y = \tan^{-1} x$

Domain: all real x

Range: $-\dfrac{\pi}{2} < y < \dfrac{\pi}{2}$

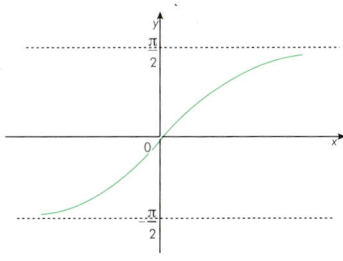

Trigonometric identities

These rules are **very important** and you must know them well enough to be able to apply them properly. It is much easier to simplify expressions, establish new identities and solve equations if you have a sound grasp of these basic results.

Pythagorean identities

Edexcel, AQA, NICCEA

$\sin^2\theta + \cos^2\theta = 1$ (1)

$\tan^2\theta + 1 = \sec^2\theta$ (Divide (1) by $\cos^2\theta$.)

$1 + \cot^2\theta = \mathrm{cosec}^2\theta$ (Divide (1) by $\sin^2\theta$.)

Compound angle formulae

Edexcel, AQA

- $\sin(A + B) = \sin A \cos B + \cos A \sin B$
- $\sin(A - B) = \sin A \cos B - \cos A \sin B$
- $\cos(A + B) = \cos A \cos B - \sin A \sin B$
- $\cos(A - B) = \cos A \cos B + \sin A \sin B$
- $\tan(A + B) = \dfrac{\tan A + \tan B}{1 - \tan A \tan B}$
- $\tan(A - B) = \dfrac{\tan A - \tan B}{1 + \tan A \tan B}$

Double angle formulae

Edexcel, AQA

You can obtain the formulae for $\cos 2A$, $\sin 2A$ and $\tan 2A$ directly from the above results by letting $B = A$.

- $\sin 2A = 2\sin A \cos A$
- $\cos 2A = \cos^2 A - \sin^2 A$ or
  $= \cos^2 A - (1 - \cos^2 A) = 2\cos^2 A - 1$ or
  $= (1 - \sin^2 A) - \sin^2 A = 1 - 2\sin^2 A$
- $\tan 2A = \dfrac{2\tan A}{1 - \tan^2 A}$

PURE 2 — TRIGONOMETRY

Half-angle formulae
Edexcel, AQA

- $\sin A = \sin\left(\frac{1}{2}A + \frac{1}{2}A\right) = 2\sin\left(\frac{1}{2}A\right)\cos\left(\frac{1}{2}A\right)$
- $\cos A = \cos\left(\frac{1}{2}A + \frac{1}{2}A\right) = \cos^2\left(\frac{1}{2}A\right) - \sin^2\left(\frac{1}{2}A\right) = 2\cos^2\left(\frac{1}{2}A\right) - 1$
$$= 1 - 2\sin^2\left(\frac{1}{2}A\right)$$
- $\tan A = \tan\left(\frac{1}{2}A + \frac{1}{2}A\right) = \dfrac{2\tan\left(\frac{1}{2}A\right)}{1 - \tan^2\left(\frac{1}{2}A\right)}$

Product to sums or differences
Edexcel

- $2\sin A \sin B = \sin(A - B) - \cos(A + B)$
- $2\cos A \cos B = \cos(A - B) + \cos(A + B)$
- $2\sin A \cos B = \sin(A - B) + \sin(A + B)$

Solving equations

There are essentially three main types of trigonometric equation that you need to be able to solve in the AS course.

Type 1: Simple trigonometric equations
Edexcel, AQA, NICCEA

There is no direct method, but there are several general rules.

- If more than two trigonometric ratios are present, convert all the ratios into one of the basic ratios (i.e. sin, cos, tan) then solve.
- Equations of this type can often be expressed as a quadratic in sin, cos or tan and then solved by algebraic methods.

Note: OCR and **WJEC** may ask you to solve simple trigonometric equations, using the identities $\dfrac{\sin\theta}{\cos\theta} = \tan\theta$ and $\sin^2\theta + \cos^2\theta = 1$.

You need to know the first three examples in the table overleaf.

PURE 2 — TRIGONOMETRY

This table shows some common examples of type 1 questions, with methods of solution and answers over the domain $0 \leq x \leq 360°$.

Question	Method of solution	Answer
$\sqrt{3}\sin x = {}^-\cos x$	Express as $\tan x = -\dfrac{1}{\sqrt{3}}$ Then solve for x.	$x = 150°, 330°$
$\cos^2 x = \dfrac{1}{2}$	Express as $\cos x = \pm\dfrac{1}{\sqrt{2}}$ Then solve for x.	$x = 45°, 135°,$ $225°, 315°$
$2\sin 3x - \sqrt{3} = 0$	Express as $\sin 3x = \dfrac{\sqrt{3}}{2}$. Then solve for x. Note that the domain for $3x$ is: $0 \leq 3x \leq 1080°$	$x = 20°, 40°,$ $140°, 160°,$ $260°, 280°$
$\cot x - 3\tan x = 2$	Express $\cot x$ as $\dfrac{1}{\tan x}$ then multiply throughout by $\tan x$ to get a quadratic in $\tan x$: $3\tan^2 x + 2\tan x - 1 = 0$ **Factorise** then solve for x.	$x = 315°, 135°,$ $18°26',$ $198°26'$

Type 2: Equations with double and half-angle results
Edexcel, AQA

- Special care should be taken to ensure that all solutions in the given domain are obtained. e.g. if $0 \leq x \leq 360°$, then for:

$\cos 2x = 1 \qquad 0 \leq 2x \leq 720°$
$\cos\left(\dfrac{x}{2}\right) = \dfrac{1}{2} \qquad 0 \leq \dfrac{x}{2} \leq 180°$

PURE 2 — TRIGONOMETRY

- Never divide by a function of x as this can remove a solution. Always factorise then solve.

This table provides common examples of type 2 questions. These are solved over the domain $0 \leq x \leq 2\pi$.

Question	Method of solution	Answer
$\sin 2x = \sin x$	Express $\sin 2x$ as $2\sin x \cos x$. Factorise and then solve for x. **Note:** Do not divide by $\sin x$ as that eliminates an answer.	$x = 0, \dfrac{\pi}{3}, \dfrac{5\pi}{6},$ $\pi, 2\pi$
$1 + \cos x = \cos\left(\dfrac{x}{2}\right)$	Express $\cos x$ as $2\cos^2\left(\dfrac{x}{2}\right) - 1$ to get a quadratic in $\cos\left(\dfrac{x}{2}\right)$: $2\cos^2\left(\dfrac{x}{2}\right) - \cos\left(\dfrac{x}{2}\right) = 0$ **Factorise** and then solve for x. **Note:** $0 \leq \dfrac{x}{2} \leq \pi$	$x = \dfrac{2\pi}{3}, \pi$
$\sin 2x = \tan x$	Express $\sin 2x$ as $2\sin x \cos x$ and $\tan x$ as $\dfrac{\sin x}{\cos x}$ and then solve. Again don't divide by $\sin x$.	$x = 0, \dfrac{\pi}{4}, \dfrac{3\pi}{4}, \pi,$ $\dfrac{5\pi}{4}, \dfrac{7\pi}{4}, 2\pi$

Type 3: Equations of the form $a\sin x \pm b\cos x = c$
Edexcel, AQA

These equations can be solved by first using the **transformation method** to rewrite the expression and then solving.

The transformation method
You can rewrite:
$a\sin x + b\cos x = R\sin(x + \alpha)$
$a\sin x - b\cos x = R\sin(x - \alpha)$
$a\cos x + b\sin x = R\cos(x - \alpha)$
$a\cos x - b\sin x = R\cos(x + \alpha)$
where in each case
$R = \sqrt{a^2 + b^2}$ and $\tan \alpha = \dfrac{b}{a}$, $0 < \alpha < 90°$.

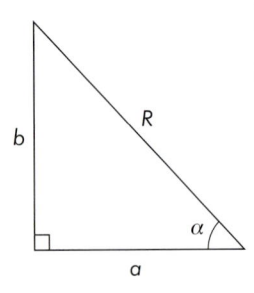

Example
Solve $\sqrt{3}\sin x - \cos x = 1$, for $0 < x < 360°$.

Solution
Let $\sqrt{3}\sin x - \cos x = R\sin(x - \alpha)$
Now $a = \sqrt{3}$, $b = 1$
$\therefore \sqrt{a^2 + b^2} = \sqrt{(\sqrt{3})^2 + (1)^2} = 2$
$\tan \alpha = \dfrac{1}{\sqrt{3}}$, i.e. $\alpha = 30°$.

The equation becomes:
$2\sin(x - 30°) = 1$
$\sin(x - 30°) = \dfrac{1}{2}$
$x - 30° = 30°, 150°$
$\therefore x = 60°, 180°$

PURE 2 — DIFFERENTIATION AND INTEGRATION

The derivative of e^x

The function e^x is unique, as it is the only function in mathematics that remains unaltered by differentiation.

- If $y = e^x$, then $\dfrac{dy}{dx} = e^x$
- In general, if $y = ae^{kx}$, then $\dfrac{dy}{dx} = ake^{kx}$

Note: The general result is needed for AQA and OCR.

The derivative of $\log_e x$

- If $y = \log_e x$, then $\dfrac{dy}{dx} = \dfrac{1}{x}$
- If $y = \log_e kx$, then $\dfrac{dy}{dx} = \dfrac{1}{x}$

The chain rule
OCR, WJEC, NICCEA

$$\dfrac{dy}{dx} = \dfrac{dy}{du} \times \dfrac{du}{dx}$$

Example

Differentiate:

(a) $(x^2 - 1)^{11}$ **(b)** $\sqrt{x^2 - 1}$

Solution

(a) Let $y = (x^2 - 1)^{11}$, $u = x^2 - 1$ $\therefore y = u^{11}$

$\dfrac{dy}{dx} = \dfrac{dy}{du} \times \dfrac{du}{dx} = 11u^{10} \times 2x = 22x(x^2 - 1)^{10}$

(b) Let $y = \sqrt{x^2 - 1}$, $u = x^2 - 1$ $\therefore y = \sqrt{u} = u^{\frac{1}{2}}$

$\dfrac{dy}{dx} = \dfrac{dy}{du} \times \dfrac{du}{dx} = \dfrac{1}{2}u^{-\frac{1}{2}} \times 2x = x(x^2 - 1)^{-\frac{1}{2}} = \dfrac{x}{\sqrt{x^2 - 1}}$

PURE 2 — DIFFERENTIATION AND INTEGRATION

Example

A spherical balloon is expanding so that the radius, r, is increasing constantly at 2 cm per second. At what rate is the volume V increasing when the radius is 8 cm?

Solution

The volume of the sphere is given by: $V = \frac{4}{3}\pi r^3$

The rate of change of the volume is $\frac{dV}{dt}$

The rate of change of the radius is $\frac{dr}{dt} = 2$

Using the chain rule: $\frac{dV}{dt} = \frac{dV}{dr} \times \frac{dr}{dt}$

$\frac{dV}{dr} = \frac{d}{dr}(\frac{4}{3}\pi r^3) = 4\pi r^2$

$\therefore \frac{dV}{dt} = 4\pi r^2 \times 2$ at $r = 8$

$= 8\pi \times 8^2 = 512\pi$ cm^3 s^{-1}

The integral of e^x

The function $y = e^x$ is also unaltered by integration.

- $\int e^x \, dx = e^x + c$
- $\int ae^x \, dx = a\int e^x \, dx = ae^x + c$
- $\int e^{kx} \, dx = \frac{1}{k}e^{kx} + c$

The integral of $\frac{1}{x}$

- $\int \frac{1}{x} \, dx = \ln|x| + c$
- $\int \frac{1}{kx} \, dx = \frac{1}{k}\int \frac{1}{x} \, dx = \frac{1}{k}\ln|x| + c$

PURE 2 — DIFFERENTIATION AND INTEGRATION

Volumes by integration
Edexcel, OCR, NICCEA

Volumes of revolution about the x-axis

The volume generated by rotating the curve $y = f(x)$ about the x-axis between $x = a$ and $x = b$ is given by:

$$V = \pi \int_a^b y^2 \, dx$$

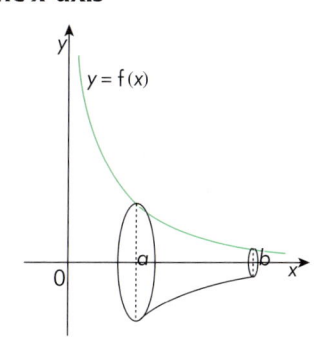

Volumes of revolution about the y-axis

The volume generated by rotating the curve $x = g(y)$ about the y-axis between $y = a$ and $y = b$ is given by:

$$V = \pi \int_a^b x^2 \, dy$$

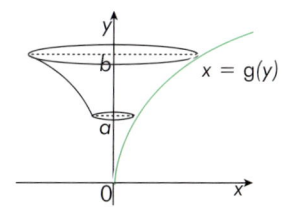

Change of sign

If f(x) is a continuous function between $x = a$ and $x = b$, and f(a) and f(b) have different signs, then a root of f(x) = 0 exists in the interval a to b.

To achieve a higher level of accuracy you can perform a decimal search. This involves finding values of the function at decimal intervals between $x = a$ and $x = b$, to trap the root in a smaller and smaller interval.

An iterative method

You can also use an iterative method to find the root(s) of non-linear equations.

Step 1: Obtain a first approximation, x_0, to the root of the equation $y = f(x)$ from a sketch of the function.

Step 2: Rewrite the equation of f(x) = 0 in the form $x = \phi(x)$.

Step 3: Set up a recurrence relation:

$x_{n+1} = \phi(x_n)$ for $n = 0, 1, 2, ...$

Step 4: Obtain the values $x_1, x_2, x_3, ...$ until they converge to a specific point correct to the required number of decimal places.

Example

Show that the equation $x^2 - 2x - 5 = 0$ has a root between 3 and 4, hence use simple iteration to find the root correct to three decimal places.

Solution

Let $f(x) = x^2 - 2x - 5$

$f(3) = {}^-2$ and $f(4) = 3$

Since f(3) and f(4) have opposite signs, there must be a root between $x = 3$ and $x = 4$.

$x^2 - 2x - 5 = 0$

$x^2 = 2x + 5$

$x = \pm\sqrt{2x + 5}$

$x = \sqrt{2x + 5}$ as the required root is positive.

We now have the equation in the form $x = \phi(x)$.

i.e. $x_{n+1} = \sqrt{2x_n + 5}$, where $n = 0, 1, 2, 3, \ldots$

Using $x_0 = 3.5$ and a calculator, we get:

$x_1 = \sqrt{2x_0 + 5} = \sqrt{2 \times 3.5 + 5} = 3.464$

$x_2 = \sqrt{2x_1 + 5} = \sqrt{2 \times 3.464 + 5} = 3.454$

$x_3 = \sqrt{2x_2 + 5} = \sqrt{2 \times 3.454 + 5} = 3.451$

$x_4 = \sqrt{2x_3 + 5} = \sqrt{2 \times 3.451 + 5} = 3.450$

$x_5 = \sqrt{2x_4 + 5} = 3.450$ (fixed point)

Thus the sequence of iterates $x_1, x_2, x_3, \ldots$ converges to 3.450. Hence the root, correct to 3 decimal places, is 3.450.

Approximations to definite integrals

Sometimes it is very difficult – if not impossible – to evaluate an integral. In such cases you can find an approximation to this value using the **trapezium rule**.

Trapezium rule

The approximate area enclosed between $y = f(x)$, the x-axis and the lines $x = a$ and $x = b$ is given by:

$$\int_a^b f(x)\,dx \approx \frac{h}{2}\left[y_0 + 2(y_1 + y_2 + \ldots + y_{n-1}) + y_n\right]$$

where h is the width of each strip.

MECHANICS — VECTORS AQA, Edexcel, OCR

Scalar and vector quantities

- A **vector** quantity (e.g. velocity, displacement) has **magnitude** (i.e. size) and **direction**.
- A **scalar** (e.g. speed, distance) has magnitude but no direction.

Vector notation

The vector from A to B is denoted by $\vec{AB}$. Vectors may also be shown as single letters (e.g. **a**, **b**, **c**) printed bold. The magnitude of vector $\vec{AB}$ is $|\vec{AB}|$ and the magnitude of vector **a** is $|\mathbf{a}|$ or a.

Operations with vectors

The equality of vectors

Vectors are equal if they have the same **magnitude** and **direction**.

The addition of vectors

The diagram shows three vectors $\vec{AB}$, $\vec{BC}$ and $\vec{AC}$ such that $\vec{AC} = \vec{AB} + \vec{BC}$.
Vector $\vec{AC}$ is the **resultant**.

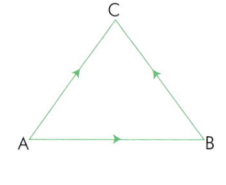

Explanation: Suppose you walked from A to B ($\vec{AB}$) then from B to C ($\vec{BC}$), following the arrows. At point C your position relative to the starting point is given by $\vec{AC}$. Thus $\vec{AB} + \vec{BC} = \vec{AC}$.

Note: The vectors $\vec{AB}$ and $\vec{BC}$ follow on from each other, then $\vec{AC}$ joins the tail of vector $\vec{AB}$ to the head of vector $\vec{BC}$. The sum of the two vectors has A as its tail and C as its head, i.e. $\vec{AB} + \vec{BC} = \vec{AC}$. This is the **triangle rule**.

The negative of a vector

The negative of a vector $\vec{AB}$ is a vector equal in length but opposite in direction.
$-\vec{AB} = \vec{BA}$

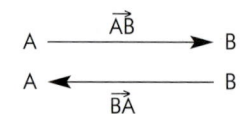

The commutative law

The commutative law holds for addition of vectors.

i.e. $\vec{AB} + \vec{BC} = \vec{BC} + \vec{AB}$

Subtraction of vectors

Given two vectors, $\vec{AB}$ and $\vec{AC}$, as shown in the diagram, their difference can be found as follows.

$$\begin{aligned}\vec{AB} - \vec{AC} &= \vec{AB} + -(\vec{AC}) \\ &= \vec{AB} + \vec{CA} \\ &= \vec{CA} + \vec{AB} \quad \text{(commutative law)} \\ &= \vec{CB} \quad \text{(triangle law)}\end{aligned}$$

This can be represented diagrammatically as follows.

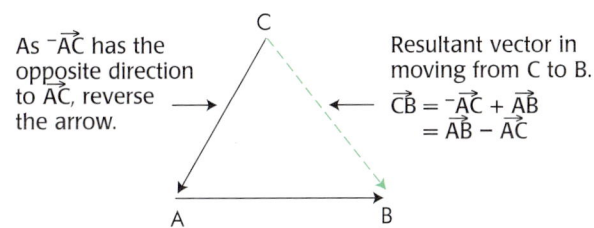

As $-\vec{AC}$ has the opposite direction to $\vec{AC}$, reverse the arrow.

Resultant vector in moving from C to B.
$\vec{CB} = -\vec{AC} + \vec{AB}$
$= \vec{AB} - \vec{AC}$

Scalar multiplication

For a given vector **a** as shown:

- 2**a** is parallel to **a**, acts in the same direction but is twice as long
- ⁻3**a** is parallel to **a**, acts in the opposite direction and is three times as long.

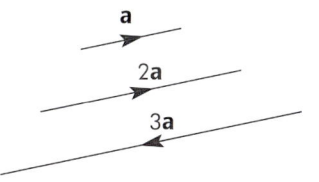

MECHANICS — VECTORS AQA, Edexcel, OCR

Example

Vectors **u** and **w** are represented by the sides of triangle ABC, as shown, and P is the midpoint of BC. Express **v** in terms of **u** and **w**.

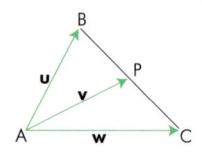

Solution

From the diagram: $\vec{AC} + \vec{CP} = \vec{AP}$ i.e. $\mathbf{w} + \vec{CP} = \mathbf{v}$ ∴ $\vec{CP} = \mathbf{v} - \mathbf{w}$

and $\vec{AP} + \vec{PB} = \vec{AB}$ i.e. $\mathbf{v} + \vec{PB} = \mathbf{u}$ ∴ $\vec{PB} = \mathbf{u} - \mathbf{v}$

But $\vec{CP} = \vec{PB}$ (P is the midpoint of CB)

∴ $\mathbf{v} - \mathbf{w} = \mathbf{u} - \mathbf{v}$ ⇒ $2\mathbf{v} = \mathbf{u} + \mathbf{w}$ ⇒ $\mathbf{v} = \frac{1}{2}(\mathbf{u} + \mathbf{w})$

Component form

It is often useful to express a vector in terms of two perpendicular **unit vectors** (i.e. their magnitude is 1), conventionally called **i** and **j**.

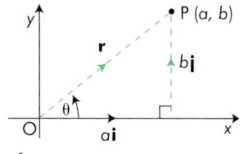

If $\mathbf{r} = a\mathbf{i} + b\mathbf{j}$ then $|\mathbf{r}| = \sqrt{a^2 + b^2}$ and $\tan\theta = \frac{b}{a}$ where θ is the angle between **r** and the positive x-axis.

Position vectors

The position vector of a point P is the vector $\vec{OP}$ where O is the origin. If P has coordinates (a, b) then its position vector is given by $\mathbf{r} = a\mathbf{i} + b\mathbf{j}$.

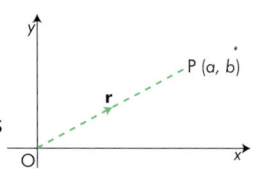

Resolving a vector

If you know the magnitude and direction of a vector, then you can use trigonometry to **resolve** it in terms of **i** and **j** components.

If a force **F** of magnitude F acts an angle θ, then $\mathbf{F} = F\cos\theta\,\mathbf{i} + F\sin\theta\,\mathbf{j}.$

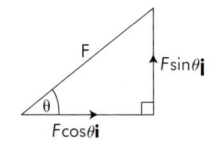

MECHANICS   **KINEMATICS**

Motion in a straight line
All Boards

Use these formulae if the acceleration of an object is constant.

- $v = u + at$
- $s = ut + \frac{1}{2}at^2$
- $s = \left(\frac{u + v}{2}\right)t$
- $v^2 = u^2 + 2as$

where: u is the initial velocity
        a is the acceleration
        s is the displacement at time t
        t is the time the object has been in motion
        v is the velocity at time t.

Graphical representation of motion
All Boards

You need to know the important features of the graphs of distance, displacement, speed, velocity and acceleration against time.

Distance–time graph

- The gradient represents speed. The steeper the line, the faster the particle is moving.
- The particle is at rest when the gradient of the curve is zero. This occurs at a stationary point.

Displacement–time graph

- The gradient represents velocity.
- A **positive** gradient means the particle is moving in a positive direction (i.e. away from its starting position). A **negative** gradient means that it is moving in a negative direction (i.e. back towards its starting position).
- The particle is stationary when the velocity is zero, i.e. at a stationary point.
- The **initial displacement** is given by the value of x at $t = 0$.

MECHANICS   KINEMATICS

Speed–time graph
- The area under the curve represents the total distance travelled.

Velocity–time graph
- The gradient represents acceleration.
- Velocity is a maximum or minimum when acceleration is zero, i.e. at a stationary point.
- The object changes direction when its velocity changes sign.
- The significance of the area under the curve depends on whether it is:
  - **entirely above the *t*-axis:**
    The area represents the total distance travelled and the displacement to the right of the origin.
  - **entirely below the *t*-axis:**
    The area represents the displacement to the left of the origin.
  - **partly above and partly below the *t*-axis:**
    The area represents the displacement to the right or left of the origin depending on whether the area above the *t*-axis (+ve) is greater, less than or equal to the area below the *t*-axis (−ve).

Acceleration–time graph
The area under the curve represents the change in velocity.

Variable acceleration

Edexcel, OCR, NECCEA

When acceleration is not constant, the constant acceleration formulae do not apply.

If displacement, x, is given as a function of time, i.e. $x = f(t)$, then:

$v = \dfrac{dx}{dt}$ Find the first derivative of x.

$a = \dfrac{dv}{dt} = \dfrac{d^2x}{dt^2}$ Find the first derivative of v or the second derivative of x.

MECHANICS   KINEMATICS

In some questions you may be given the acceleration and asked to find v and x. You need to use integration.

$v = \int a \, dt + c_1$ Integrate acceleration to find the velocity.

$x = \int v \, dt + c_2$ Integrate velocity to find the displacement.

Note: c_1 and c_2 are constants which must be calculated from information provided in the question.

Using vectors
AQA, Edexcel, OCR

The constant and variable acceleration formulae work equally well in two or three dimensions, using vectors.

Example
A particle has position vector $\mathbf{r} = 4t^3\mathbf{i} + t^2\mathbf{j}$.
Find its velocity and acceleration at $t = 1$.

Solution
$$\mathbf{v} = \frac{d\mathbf{r}}{dt}$$
$$= \frac{d}{dt}(4t^3\mathbf{i} + t^2\mathbf{j})$$
$$= 12t^2\mathbf{i} + 2t\mathbf{j}$$

$$\mathbf{a} = \frac{d\mathbf{v}}{dt}$$
$$= \frac{d}{dt}(12t^2\mathbf{i} + 2t\mathbf{j})$$
$$= 24t\mathbf{i} + 2\mathbf{j}$$

At $t = 1$, $\mathbf{v} = 12\mathbf{i} + 2\mathbf{j}$, $\mathbf{a} = 24\mathbf{i} + 2\mathbf{j}$.

Mechanics — Kinematics

Projectiles
AQA

In the study of projectiles in your AS course you will ignore air resistance and assume that the only force acting on the particle is its weight, vertically downwards. The acceleration due to gravity is taken to be constant, with a value of 9.8 m s^{-2}. The horizontal and vertical components of the motion need to be analysed separately.

Example

A projectile is fired with velocity 840 m s^{-1} at 60° to the horizontal. Find the maximum height attained by the projectile.

Solution

Vertically: $u = 840 \sin 60° = 420\sqrt{3}$, $a = {}^-9.8$.

At maximum height $v = 0$.

i.e. $v = u + at$
$0 = 420\sqrt{3} - 9.8t$
$t = 74.23\ldots$

Now, $s = ut + \frac{1}{2}at^2$

$= 420\sqrt{3} \times 74.23 + \frac{1}{2} \times {}^-9.8 \times (74.23)^2$

$= 27\,000$

∴ the maximum height is 27 000 m.

MECHANICS — STATICS

Resolving forces
All Boards

You need to be able to resolve forces into horizontal and vertical components. An important example is an object on an inclined plane.

The forces acting at P are:

- its weight W downwards
- friction F along the slope
- the normal reaction R, at right angles to the slope.

Resolving forces at P:

- down the slope: $W \sin \theta = F$
- at right angles to the slope: $W \cos \theta = R$

Resultant forces
All Boards

The resultant force on an object is the combined effect of all the forces acting on it. It can be found by vector addition.

Follow these steps to find the resultant when more than two forces that are not acting at right angles are involved.

Step 1: Use trigonometry to resolve each force into a horizontal and a vertical component. Make sure you allow for *minus signs* – decide in advance which direction (both horizontally and vertically) is positive or negative.

Step 2: Add up the components to find the net vertical and horizontal forces acting on the object.

Step 3: Draw up a vector diagram and hence calculate the magnitude and direction of the resultant force.

Mechanics — Statics

Equilibrium
All Boards

A body is in equilibrium if there is no resultant force on it. This occurs if it is not moving or is moving at constant velocity (Newton's first law).

Friction
All Boards

Friction occurs whenever a 'rough' surface is involved. You need to know the following facts relating to friction.

- It always acts to oppose the motion.
- If there is no tendency to motion there is no friction.
- Friction will increase as necessary to prevent motion, but it can only increase up to its **limiting value**, which is given by:

  $F = \mu R$

  where: μ = coefficient of friction
  R = normal reaction

- When a body is in motion, friction assumes its limiting value so $F = \mu R$.

Example

An object of weight 80 N rest on a rough horizontal surface. A horizontal force of 25 N is applied so that the object is about to slide. Find the value of the coefficient of friction.

Solution

Resolving vertically: $R = 80$

Resolving horizontally: $F = 25$

Friction is limiting $\therefore\ F = \mu R$

$$25 = \mu 80$$
$$\mu = \frac{25}{80} = 0.3125$$

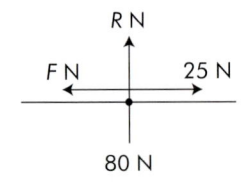

Mechanics — Statics

Moments

All Boards

The moment of a force about a point is a measure of the turning effect of the force about that point.

Moment = force × perpendicular distance from that point

When more than one force is involved, the **resultant moment** about a point is found by adding the separate moments. One direction (i.e. clockwise or anti-clockwise) is taken to be positive and the other negative.

An object is in **equilibrium** if the resultant force and moment acting on it are zero.

Example

The diagram shows a rod AB in equilibrium. Find l and F.

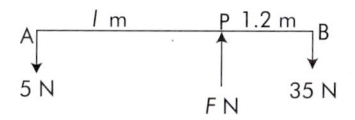

```
     l m         P  1.2 m
  A|——————————————|————————|B
   ↓              ↑        ↓
   5 N           F N       35 N
```

Solution

Resolving vertically: $F = 5 + 35 = 40$ N

Taking moments about P (which may be written as $M(P)$) gives:

$5l - 35 \times 1.2 = 0$

$\qquad 5l = 42$

$\therefore l = 8.4$ m

MECHANICS — STATICS

Centre of mass

AQA, Edexcel, WJEC

For n separate masses $m_1, m_2, \ldots, m_n$ the position of the centre of mass from O is given by:

$$\bar{x} = \frac{m_1 x_1 + m_2 x_2 + \ldots + m_n x_n}{m_1 + m_2 + \ldots + m_n} = \frac{\sum_{i=1}^{n} m_i x_i}{\sum_{i=1}^{n} m_i}$$

For a **two-dimensional shape**, the position of the centre of mass is given by $(\bar{x}, \bar{y})$, where $\bar{x}$ is as above and $\bar{y}$ is given by:

$$\bar{y} = \frac{\sum_{i=1}^{n} m_i y_i}{\sum_{i=1}^{n} m_i}$$

Example

Find the distance of the centre of mass from O.

Solution

$$\bar{x} = \frac{m_1 x_1 + m_2 x_2 + m_3 x_3}{m_1 + m_2 + m_3}$$

$$= \frac{13 \times 1 + 2 \times 2.5 + 8 \times 3.5}{13 + 2 + 8} = \frac{46}{23} = 2$$

The centre of mass is 2 m from O.

| MECHANICS | DYNAMICS |

Newton's second law
All Boards

Newton's second law states that: $F = ma$

where: F = resultant force in the direction in which the body is moving
m = mass of the body
a = acceleration

Note: The resultant force perpendicular to the motion will be zero: a fact that is commonly required in solving these problems.

Example
A box of mass 5 kg is being towed by forces $(9\mathbf{i} - 2\mathbf{j} + \mathbf{k})$ N and $(\mathbf{i} - 3\mathbf{j} + \mathbf{k})$ N. Find the acceleration produced.

Solution
$F = ma$ i.e. $(9\mathbf{i} - 2\mathbf{j} + \mathbf{k}) + (\mathbf{i} - 3\mathbf{j} + \mathbf{k}) = 5\mathbf{a}$
$10\mathbf{i} - 5\mathbf{j} + 2\mathbf{k} = 5\mathbf{a}$
$\mathbf{a} = 2\mathbf{i} - \mathbf{j} + 0.4\mathbf{k}$

∴ the acceleration of the box is $2\mathbf{i} - \mathbf{j} + 0.4\mathbf{k}$ m s^{-2}.

Connected objects
All Boards

This section relates to two objects connected by a light inextensible string. By Newton's third law, the tension in the string acts equally on both objects but in opposite directions.

Since the string is light, there is no need to consider its mass and, since it is inextensible, the connected objects must have the same speed and acceleration while the string is taut.

Newton's laws can also be applied to objects connected by light inextensible strings passing over light frictionless pulleys. Under these ideal conditions, it may be assumed that the strings do not stretch and the magnitude of the tension throughout the string is constant.

Mechanics

Dynamics

Example

Two particles A (3 kg) and B (5 kg) are connected by a light inextensible string passing over a light frictionless pulley. Particle A is on a smooth horizontal table whilst particle B hangs freely. Taking $g = 10$ m s^{-2}, find the tension in the string.

Solution

The first step is to draw a diagram showing the forces acting on each particle.

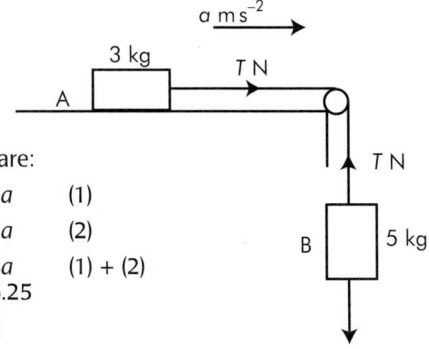

The equations of motion are:

For particle A: $\quad T = 3a \quad$ (1)

For particle B: $\; 50 - T = 5a \quad$ (2)

$\qquad\qquad\quad 50 = 8a \quad$ (1) + (2)

$\qquad\qquad\qquad a = 6.25$

$\therefore T = 3 \times 6.25 = 18.75$ N

The tension in the string is 18.75 N.

Momentum

All Boards

The momentum of a particle is a vector quantity. It is given by:

momentum = m**v**

where: m is the mass of the particle (kg)
$\quad\quad\;$ **v** is the velocity (m s^{-1})

It two particles collide, then the principle of conservation of momentum states that:

total momentum before impact = total momentum after impact

$m_1u_1 + m_2u_2 = m_1v_1 + m_2v_2$

where: m_1 is the mass of the first particle
m_2 is the mass of the second particle
u_1 is the speed of the first particle before impact
u_2 is the speed of the second particle before impact
v_1 is the speed of the first particle after impact
v_2 is the speed of the second particle after impact.

Impulse
Edexcel, WJEC, NICCEA

Impulse is a vector quantity. It is given by:

impulse = change in momentum

$I = Ft = m(v - u)$

where: F = the force in N
t = time in seconds
m = mass in kg
u = initial speed
v = resultant speed.

Example

An object A of mass 8 kg moving with speed 20 m s^{-1} collides with another particle B of mass 4 kg, which is at rest. After the impact both particles move together with the same speed, v m s^{-1}.

(a) Find the value of v.
(b) Find the magnitude of the impulse exerted on B by A during impact.

Solution

(a) $m_1u_1 + m_2u_2 = m_1v_1 + m_2v_2$

where $m_1 = 8$, $u_1 = 20$, $m_2 = 4$, $u_2 = 0$, $v_1 = v_2 = v$

i.e. $8 \times 20 + 4 \times 0 = 8v + 4v$
$160 = 12v$
$v = 13.3$ m s^{-1} to 1 d.p.

(b) Impulse = $m(v - u) = 4(13.3 - 0) = 53.3$ N

STATISTICS — REPRESENTING DATA All Boards

Basic statistical formulae

- Mode = most common data value
- Mean = $\dfrac{\text{total of all data values}}{\text{number of data values}} = \dfrac{\sum x}{n} = \dfrac{\sum xf}{\sum f}$
- Median = middle value, when values are arranged in order of size

Note: If the number of data values is even, then the median is the mean of the two middle values.

Statistical notation

x = data value
f = frequency
cf = cumulative frequency
$\bar{x}$ = mean

$\sum$ = sum
$\sum f$ = sum of frequency column
xf = (data value) × (frequency)
$\sum xf$ = sum of xf column

Measures of spread

Use the **range**, the **interquartile range** and the **standard deviation** to measure the spread of a set of data.

Measures of spread are important for describing the extent of dispersion in the data.

Range

The range is the difference between the highest and lowest data values.

Range = highest value − lowest value

The range does not provide a lot of information on the spread, as it depends only on the extreme values.

STATISTICS — REPRESENTING DATA All Boards

Interquartile range

The **interquartile range** is the difference between the upper quartile (Q_3) and the lower quartile (Q_1).

$$IQR = Q_3 - Q_1$$

Note: Upper quartile is the value $\frac{3}{4}$ (75%) of the way into the data.

Note: Lower quartile is the value $\frac{1}{4}$ (25%) of the way into the data.

The interquartile range is the spread of the middle half of the data values.

A large interquartile range indicates that much of the data is widely spread about the median.

A small interquartile range indicates that much of the data is concentrated about the median.

The quartiles may also be used to indicate whether the data values are **positively skewed** ($Q_2 - Q_1 < Q_3 - Q_2$) or **negatively skewed** ($Q_2 - Q_1 > Q_3 - Q_2$).

In most cases the IQR is a more reliable measure of the spread than the range, as it is not as affected by exceptional values.

Standard deviation

In practice, the range is rarely used as the spread of a sample. The standard deviation is more commonly used as a measure of how spread the data is relative to the mean.

$$\text{Standard deviation} = \sqrt{\text{variance}}$$

$$= \sqrt{\frac{\sum x^2}{n} - \bar{x}^2} \quad \text{or}$$

$$= \sqrt{\frac{\sum f x^2}{n} - \bar{x}^2}$$

A large standard deviation means the scores are widely spread, while a smaller standard deviation means that the scores are closer to the mean.

STATISTICS   REPRESENTING DATA All Boards

Statistical diagrams

Statistical diagrams can be very useful in providing additional information about the data.

Box and whisker plot

A box and whisker plot provides a quick 'snap shot' of the spread of a distribution.

It uses five-number summary statistics.

Example

Consider a set of scores with a lowest score of 5, highest score of 25, median of 16.5, upper quartile 22 and lower quartile 12.5.

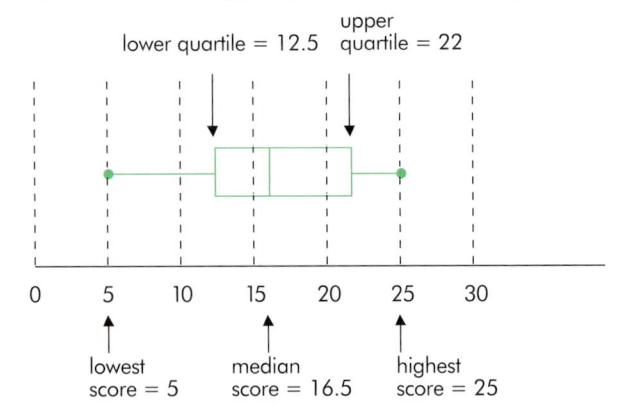

Back-to-back stem plots

The back-to-back stem plot is a simple extension of the regular stem plot. It is used to compare the distribution of two sets of values for the same variable.

STATISTICS — REPRESENTING DATA All Boards

Example

Test results (out of 50) for class A and class B are shown below.

Class A: 15 24 20 40 43 38 9 28 33 31 47 33 30 27 18
Class B: 49 36 39 28 10 26 30 32 34 42 41 27 2 19 50

i Draw an ordered back-to-back stem plot for the two data sets. For each data set indicate the extreme values, median and lower and upper quartiles.

ii Which class performed better overall? Give reasons.

Solution

i

Class A		stem	Class B	
Minimum = 9	9	0	2	Minimum = 2
$Q_1 = 20$	8 5	1	0 9	$Q_1 = 26$
$m = 30$	8 7 4 0	2	6 7 8	$m = 32$
$Q_3 = 38$	8 3 3 1 0	3	0 2 4 6 9	$Q_3 = 41$
Maximum = 47	7 3 0	4	1 2 9	Maximum = 50
$Q_3 - Q_1 = 18$		5	0	$Q_3 - Q_1 = 15$

ii Class B performed better overall. Reasons include:

- higher median score (*m*) of 32 for class B
- the IQR for class B (15) is smaller, indicating that the results are more concentrated around the median
- at the top end, class B performed better, with two students scoring full or near full marks.

Histograms and frequency polygons

You need to be able to set up a frequency distribution table and, from that, draw the:

- histogram of the data and its associated frequency polygon
- cumulative frequency histogram of the data and its associated cumulative frequency polygon.

In certain cases you may first need to group the data into class intervals before you can construct a frequency distribution table.

STATISTICS
REPRESENTING DATA All Boards

Example

Twenty students were each given a coin and asked to toss it four times. Each student then recorded the number of heads attained. The results were as follows.

2 3 1 2 2 2 4 2 3 1
3 1 2 3 1 0 1 2 4 2

i Construct a frequency distribution table for this data.

ii Construct:
  a a frequency histogram and its associated frequency polygon.
  b a cumulative frequency histogram and its associated cumulative frequency polygon.

iii Find the range, mode, median, mean and interquartile range of the data.

Solution

i

Score (x)	Tally	Frequency (f)	Cumulative frequency (cf)	xf
0	|	1	1	0
1	||||	5	6	5
2	|||| |||	8	14	16
3	||||	4	18	12
4	||	2	20	8
		20		41

ii a

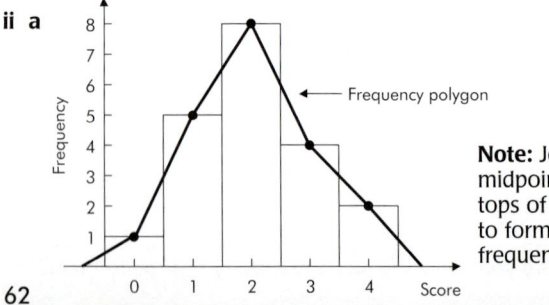

Note: Join the midpoints of the tops of the columns to form the frequency polygon.

b

Cumulative frequency polygon

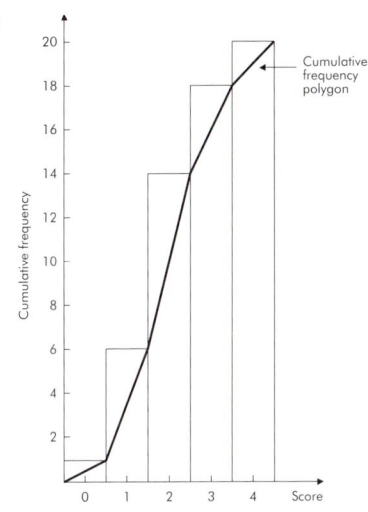

Note: Join the end points of the columns to form the cumulative frequency polygon.

iii Range = highest observation − lowest observation
= 4 − 0 = 4

Mode is the score that occurs most often. In this case it is 2 (eight observations).

Median is the middle observation. Since there are an even number of observations, the median is the average of the two middle values.

Average of the 10th and 11th observations = $\frac{2+2}{2} = 2$

Mean = $\frac{\sum xf}{\sum f} = \frac{41}{20} = 2.05$

Interquartile range = $Q_3 - Q_1$

Q_1 is the value in the middle of the lower half of the data i.e. the average of the 5th and 6th observations, which is 1.
Q_3 is the value in the middle of the upper half of the data i.e. the average of the 15th and 16th observations, which is 3.

∴ IQR = 3 − 1 = 2

STATISTICS · PROBABILITY

Venn diagrams
All Boards

You can use Venn diagrams to represent and interpret combined events. Outcomes are the possible results of events.

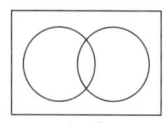

A∪B — A∪B represents the outcomes for A or B or both.

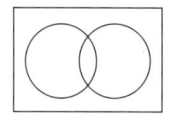

A∩B — A∩B represent the outcomes for both A and B.

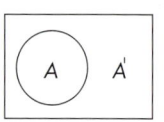

A' represents those outcomes that do not belong to A.

The probability that an outcome does not occur
All Boards

If P(A) is the probability that outcome A occurs and P(A') is the probability that the outcome does not occur, then:

P(A') = 1 − P(A)

Mutually exclusive outcomes or events
All Boards

A and B are **mutually exclusive** if they cannot happen at the same time.

If A and B are mutually exclusive, then:

P(A∩B) = 0

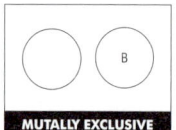

MUTALLY EXCLUSIVE

The addition rule of probability
All Boards

Before applying the addition rule of probability, you must first identify whether the outcomes or events are **mutually exclusive**.

Statistics — Probability

A and B are **not** mutually exclusive
if they have some outcomes in common.

If A and B are **mutually exclusive** then:

$P(A \cup B) = P(A) + P(B)$

If A and B are **not mutually exclusive** then:

$P(A \cup B) = P(A) + P(B) - P(A \cap B)$

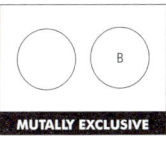

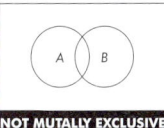

Independent events
All Boards

A and B are described as **independent events** if the probability that either event occurs is not affected by whether the other event has already occurred.

The multiplication rule of probability
All Boards

If A and B are independent events, then:

$P(A \cap B) = P(A) \times P(B)$

Tree diagrams
All Boards

A tree diagram is a useful tool for representing the probabilities of combined events. It is also helpful in identifying the sample space.

The following rules apply to tree diagrams.

- **Multiply along the branches** to determine the probability of each outcome.
- If more than one path satisfies the conditions of a problem, add these probabilities.
- All the probabilities along all the branches **sum to 1**.

STATISTICS PROBABILITY

Example

The probability that Sonya passes a particular maths test is 0.9. If she sits three maths tests, find the probability she passes at least two tests.

Solution

Let $p\ (= 0.9)$ and $q\ (= 0.1)$ be respectively the probabilities of passing (S) and failing ($\bar{S}$). The tree diagram is as follows.

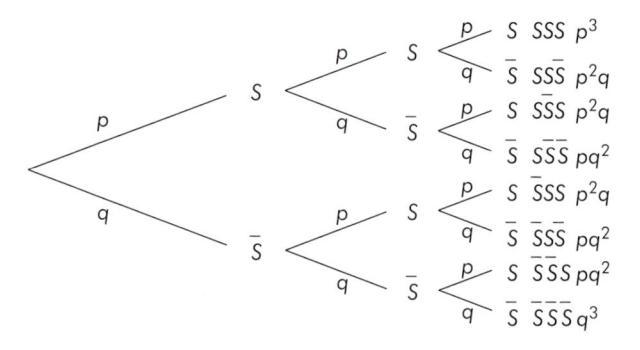

```
                              p   S   SSS    p³
                      p   S <
                  S <         q   S̄   SSS̄   p²q
              p <     q   S̄ < p   S   SS̄S   p²q
                              q   S̄   SS̄S̄   pq²
          <
              q       p   S < p   S   S̄SS   p²q
                  S̄ <         q   S̄   S̄SS̄   pq²
                      q   S̄ < p   S   S̄S̄S   pq²
                              q   S̄   S̄S̄S̄   q³
```

P(passes at least 2) = P(SSS) + P($SS\bar{S}$) + P($S\bar{S}S$) + P($\bar{S}SS$)
$= p^3 + 3p^2q$
$= 0.972$

Conditional probability

All Boards

Conditional probability represents the probability that a particular event occurs given that a particular outcome is known.

$P(A|B)$ is a conditional probability: it represents the probability of A occurring **conditionally** upon B having occurred. It is given by:

$P(A|B) = \dfrac{P(A \cap B)}{P(B)}$

Combinatorics

Edexcel, OCR

You need to be able to find the number of different arrangements of objects in certain situations.

Ordered arrangements

The number of different possible arrangements using n different objects is $n!$.

$n! = n(n-1)(n-2) \ldots 3.2.1$

Note: $n!$ is the product of all the consecutive numbers, from 1 up to and including n.

Arrangements with indistinguishable elements

The number of different ways of arranging n objects of which k are alike and another l are alike, is given by:

$$\frac{n!}{k! l! \ldots}$$

Permutations

A permutation is an ordered arrangement of a number of objects. The number of permutations of n different objects, taking r at a time, is given by:

$$_nP_r = \frac{n!}{(n-r)!}$$

Combinations

A combination is a group of objects selected without regard to their order. The number of combinations of r items selected from n different objects is given by:

$$_nC_r = \frac{n!}{(n-r)! r!}$$

STATISTICS — DISCRETE RANDOM VARIABLES

Discrete random variables
All Boards

A **discrete random variable** may take on only a countable number of distinct values such as 0, 1, 2, 3, ... (for example the number of children in a family).

In the usual notation:

- X (capital, by convention) is used to denote the random variable
- the probability that X takes a particular value x is equal to the sum of the probabilities of the sample points for which $X = x$. It is written as $P(X = x)$ or simply $P(x)$.

The listing of the possible values for X and their associated probabilities is called a **probability distribution**.

The properties of a probability distribution are:

$0 \leq P(X = x) \leq 1$ Probability of each outcome has a value from 0 to 1.

$\sum P(X = x) = 1$ Sum of probabilities of all possible outcomes is 1.

$P(x_i \leq X \leq x_j) = \sum_{x=x_i}^{x_j} P(X = x)$

Expected values
All Boards

The expected value represents the average outcome of an experiment. It is denoted by $E(X)$.

If X is a discrete random variable with possible values of x_1, x_2, ..., x_n and the corresponding probabilities of $P(X = x_1)$, $P(X = x_2)$, ..., $P(X = x_n)$, then the **expected value** of X is given by:

$$E(X) = \sum_{i=1}^{n} x_i P(X = x_i)$$

STATISTICS — DISCRETE RANDOM VARIABLES

Expected value of a function

The expected value of a function of a random variable is found in a similar way. In general, if g(X) is some function of the random variable X then:

$$E[g(X)] = \sum_{\text{all } x} g(x)P(X = x)$$

Expectation theorems

If a and b are constants and X is a random variable, then:

$$E(aX) = aE(X) \quad E(aX + b) = aE(X) + b$$

Variance and standard deviation of a random variable

All Boards

The **standard deviation** (sd) of a random variable X measures the spread of the probability distribution about its mean μ, and is denoted by σ. The **variance** of X is denoted by Var(X) or σ^2. They can be calculated as follows.

$$\sigma^2 = \text{Var}(X) = E(X^2) - \mu^2, \text{ where } \mu = E(X)$$

$$\sigma = \text{sd}(X) = \sqrt{\text{Var}(x)}$$

In general:

If X is a random variable and a and b are constants, then:

$$\text{Var}(aX + b) = a^2 \text{Var}(X) \quad \text{and} \quad \text{sd}(aX + b) = a\,\text{sd}(X)$$

Discrete uniform distribution

All Boards

A discrete uniform distribution is one in which every possible value of the variable has the same probability. The probability that X takes the value x is given by:

$$P(X = x) = \frac{1}{n} \text{ for } x = 1, 2, 3, ..., n$$

$$E(X) = \frac{1}{2}(n + 1) \text{ and } \text{Var}(X) = \frac{1}{12}(n^2 - 1)$$

STATISTICS — DISCRETE RANDOM VARIABLES

The binomial probability distribution

AQA, OCR, WJEC, NICCEA

Binomial distributions model discrete random variables.

Typically, a binomial random variable is the number of successes in a series of trials.

A **binomial experiment** has the following characteristics.

- It consists of n identical trials.
- There are just two outcomes of each trial; success and failure.
- All trials are statistically independent.
- All the trials have the same probability of success, which is equal to p. The probability of failure is q where $q = 1 - p$.
- The number of successes in n trials is denoted by x.

If a discrete random variable X follows a binomial distribution with parameters n and p denoted by $X \sim \text{Bi}(n, p)$, then:

$$P(X = x) = {}_nC_x q^{n-x} p^x$$

where $x = 0, 1, 2, ..., n$

The expected value and variance of the binomial distribution are given by:

$$E(X) = np \text{ and } \text{Var}(X) = npq$$

Example

At a particular factory, 5% of all light bulbs produced are defective. A sample of 40 light bulbs is selected at random. Find:

i the mean number of defective bulbs selected

ii the variance of the number of defective bulbs selected.

Solution

i p = probability of a defective bulb = 0.05
$q = 1 - p = 1 - 0.05 = 0.95$
$n = 40$

If X represents the number of defective bulbs, then:

$X \sim \text{Bi}(n = 40, p = 0.05)$

$\therefore \mu = E(X) = np$
$ = 40 \times 0.05$
$ = 2$

Thus the mean number of defective bulbs selected is 2.

ii $\sigma^2 = npq$
$ = 40 \times 0.05 \times 0.95$
$ = 1.9$

Thus the variance of the number of defective bulbs is 1.9.

The Poisson distribution
AQA, WJEC, NICCEA

The Poisson distribution is used to model the number of occurrences of a particular event in a prescribed time or space interval.

If a discrete random variable X follows a Poisson distribution with parameter λ denoted by $X \sim \text{Po}(\lambda)$, then:

$P(X = x) = \dfrac{e^{-\lambda}\lambda^x}{x!}$ for $x = 0, 1, 2, \ldots$

$E(X) = \lambda$ and $\text{Var}(X) = \lambda$

where λ is the mean number of occurrences per unit time or space.

The geometric distribution
OCR

The geometric distribution is used to model the number of independent trials needed before a success occurs. If a discrete random variable X follows a geometric distribution with parameter p then:

$P(X = x) = p(1 - p)^{x-1}$ for $x = 1, 2, 3, \ldots$

where p is the probability of success.

STATISTICS — THE NORMAL DISTRIBUTION

Continuous random variables

AQA, Edexcel, NICCEA

A continuous random variable may take any value within a prescribed interval. A **probability density function** (pdf) describes how the probability is distributed over this interval. If a pdf is denoted by f(x), then:

$$\int_{-\infty}^{\infty} f(x)\, dx = 1 \quad \text{and} \quad P(a \leq X \leq b) = \int_{a}^{b} f(x)\, dx$$

The normal distribution

AQA, Edexcel, NICCEA

If a continuous random variable X follows a normal distribution, then the standard normal variable Z is used to calculate probabilities based on the normal distribution where:

$$Z = \frac{X - \mu}{\sigma} \quad \text{and} \quad Z \sim N(0, 1)$$

Example

The life of an electric drill follows a normal distribution with mean 8 years and standard deviation 1.25 years. The manufacturer will replace drills that fail while under warranty, but is willing to replace only 5% of the drills. How long should the warranty period be?

Solution

P(drill fails and is replaced) = 0.05 i.e. $0.05 = P(Z \leq z_1)$

Now, $0.05 = P(Z \leq z_1) = 1 - P(Z \leq z_2)$ {by symmetry}

i.e. $z_2 = 1.6449$ {use CND table}

∴ $z_1 = {}^-1.6449$ {by symmetry}

Now, $Z = \frac{X - \mu}{\sigma} \Rightarrow {}^-1.6449 = \frac{x_1 - 8}{1.25}$

${}^-1.6449 \times 1.25 = x_1 - 8$

∴ $x_1 = 8 - 1.6449 \times 1.25 = 5.943\,875 \approx 6$

The warranty period should be extended to approximately 6 years.

STATISTICS — CORRELATION AND REGRESSION

Correlation

AQA, Edexcel, OCR

A scatter plot is used to show the **relationship** between two sets of data.

There may either be a linear (straight line) relationship or a non-linear (curved) relationship between the two variables.

The **correlation coefficient**, r, measures the extent of the linear association between the two variables. One way to calculate the correlation is to use the product-moment correlation coefficient formula:

$$r = \frac{S_{xy}}{\sqrt{S_{xx}S_{yy}}}, \quad -1 \leq r \leq 1$$

where: $S_{xx} = \sum x^2 - n\bar{x}^2$
$S_{yy} = \sum y^2 - n\bar{y}^2$
$S_{xy} = \sum xy - n\bar{x}\bar{y}$

Note: this formula is used when both variables are normally distributed.

An alternative method to measure correlation is given by Spearman's rank correlation coefficient, r_s.

The values for each variable must first be ranked in descending order. For equal values, the average positional value is used.

At each data point, the difference, d, in the rank of the two variables is calculated. This is then used to find r_s.

$$r_s = 1 - \frac{6\sum d^2}{n^3 - n}, \quad -1 \leq r_s \leq 1$$

Degree of correlation

The degree of correlation between two variables may be described as weak, moderate or strong, depending on the **magnitude** of r (i.e. ignoring the sign).

STATISTICS — CORRELATION AND REGRESSION

A relationship is considered to be:
- **weak** if $0 \leq r \leq 0.49$
- **moderate** if $0.5 \leq r \leq 0.74$
- **strong** if $0.75 \leq r \leq 1$

Note: A magnitude for r of 1 represents perfect correlation whilst a value of 0 represents no correlation between the variables.

The **sign** of r determines whether the relationship is positive (+) or negative (−).

Regression
AQA, Edexcel, OCR

Whereas correlation is calculated to determine whether two variables are interrelated, regression is about the kind of relationship which exists as indicated by the equation of the **regression line**.

Regression lines are used for predicting the values of one of the variables. The equation of such a line is of the form:

$y = ax + b$

where a and b can be determined.

The least squares regression line

This is commonly used by statisticians to determine the line of best fit through the data. It is designed to **minimise** the distance between the plotted points and the resulting trendline.

- The least squares regression line of **y on x** is given by: $y = a + bx$
  where: $b = \dfrac{S_{xy}}{S_{xx}}$ and $a = \bar{y} - b\bar{x}$

  Use this equation to predict y-values for given values of x.

- The least squares regression line of **x on y** is given by: $x = c + dy$
  where: $d = \dfrac{S_{xy}}{S_{xx}}$ and $c = \bar{x} - d\bar{y}$

  Use this equation to predict x-values for given values of y.

DECISION MATHEMATICS   **ALGORITHMS**

Introducing algorithms

AQA, OCR, Edexcel

An algorithm is a set of instructions used to solve a problem. It is performed by breaking the algorithm into steps and following them, one at a time.

The bubble sort

Edexcel, OCR

The bubble sort is an algorithm for sorting elements in a list in a particular order.

Step 1: Compare each pair of adjacent elements, moving from left to right, and switch them if they are in the wrong order.

Step 2: Continue until you reach the end. This completes the first **pass** through the list.

Step 3: Repeat the process until a pass produces no change.

The quick sort

Edexcel, OCR

Step 1: Take the first element in the list as the **pivot**.

Step 2: Now with the other elements, place any number less than the pivot to one side and the remaining to the other side.

Step 3: Repeat steps 1 and 2 for each sub-list of elements on either side of the pivot until each one contains a single element.

Note: For **Edexcel** the middle value is chosen as the pivot.

The shuttle sort

Edexcel, OCR

The shuttle sort is an alternative algorithm for sorting elements in a list in a particular order.

Step 1: Compare the first two elements in the list and place them in the correct order.

Step 2: Introduce the next element in the list and compare it with those already sorted. Shuttle it along the line so that it is in the correct position compared with the elements already sorted.

Step 3: Repeat step 2 until all elements in the list have been considered and shuttled to their correct position.

Binary search
Edexcel

To find an element in an ordered list, follow these steps.

Step 1: Find the element in the middle of the list. If it matches, stop. If not, use the middle term to ascertain the half in which the required element lies.

Step 2: Repeat step 1 for the selected half until the required element is found.

Bin packing
Edexcel, OCR

The bin packing algorithm is designed to pack boxes of different heights but equal cross-sections into bins so as to **minimise** the number of bins used. There is no single method, but the following three algorithms provide a good solution.

First-fit algorithm

Place boxes in the order given into the first then next available bin.

Full-bin algorithm

Fill each bin with a combination of boxes that will fill it. Then use the first-fit algorithm on the remaining boxes.

First-fit decreasing algorithm

First arrange the boxes in decreasing order of size. Then use the first-fit algorithm, commencing with the largest box.

Decision Mathematics — Graphs and Networks

Defining terms

AQA, Edexcel, OCR

- An **undirected graph** is a set of points, called **vertices**, connected by lines called **edges**.
- A **complete graph** is one in which each vertex is connected to every other vertex.
- A **subgraph** is a subset containing vertices and edges of a graph.

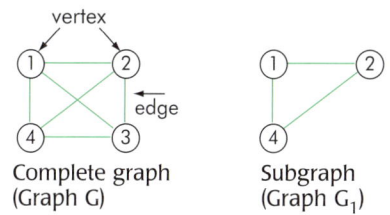

Complete graph
(Graph G)

Subgraph
(Graph G_1)

- The number of edges connected to a vertex is called its **order** or **degree**. It is denoted by deg(vertex). A vertex is classified as **odd** or **even**, depending on whether its order is odd or even.
- **Multiple** (or parallel) **edges** are two or more edges connecting the same two vertices.
- A **loop** is an edge that connects the vertex back to itself. A loop contributes 2 to the degree of a vertex.

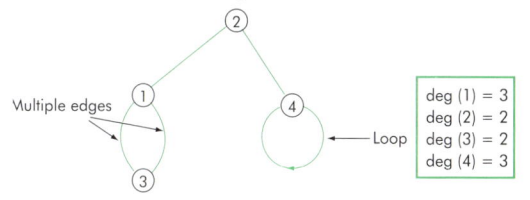

deg (1) = 3
deg (2) = 2
deg (3) = 2
deg (4) = 3

- A **path** is a finite sequence of edges such that the end vertex of one edge is the start vertex of the next edge. No edge is included more than once. The number of edges used in a path is the **length** of the path.

DECISION MATHEMATICS — GRAPHS AND NETWORKS

- A **connected graph** is one in which you can go from one vertex to another by following some path along the edges (i.e. a connected graph is in 'one piece').

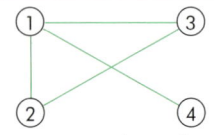

Connected graph

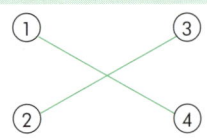

Disconnected graph (No path from vertex 1 to vertex 2)

- A **circuit** or **cycle** is a path that starts and finishes at the same vertex. No edge is included more than once.

  In the graph on the right:
  1 − 2 − 3 − 4 − 1 is a circuit
  1 − 2 − 4 − 3 − 5 − 1 is a circuit etc.

- A **planar graph** is a graph where no two edges meet except at a vertex. Graph K is planar.

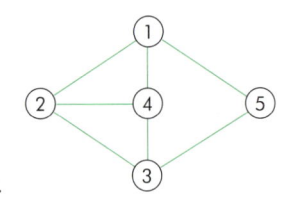

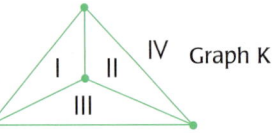

- An **Euler path** is one that covers all the edges of the graph exactly once. If it starts and ends on the same vertex it is an **Eulerian cycle**.

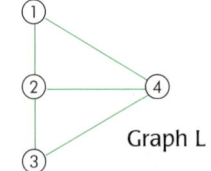

Graph L

The path (2 − 3 − 4 − 2 − 1 − 4) is an **Euler path**.

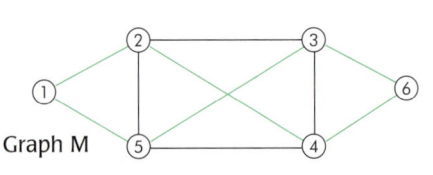

Graph M

The path (5 − 2 − 3 − 4 − 5 − 3 − 6 − 4 − 2 − 1 − 5) is an **Eulerian cycle**.

DECISION MATHEMATICS — GRAPHS AND NETWORKS

- A **Hamilton path** is one that covers all the vertices of the graph exactly once. If it starts and ends on the same vertex it is a **Hamiltonian cycle**.

  For graph L: (1 − 2 − 4 − 3) is a **Hamilton path**.
  For graph M: (1 − 2 − 3 − 6 − 4 − 5 − 1) is a **Hamiltonian cycle**.

- A **tree** is a graph with no cycles.
- A **spanning tree** is a **subgraph** that contains all the vertices of the original graph and is a tree.

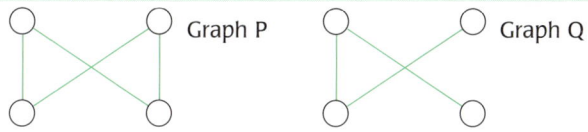

  Graph P   Graph Q

  Graph Q is a subgraph of Graph P and since it is also a tree, thus Graph Q is a **spanning tree**.

- A **network** is a graph that has a number (**weight**) associated with every edge.
- A **minimum spanning tree** of a network is a spanning tree of minimum possible weight.
- A **maximum spanning tree** of a network is a spanning tree of maximum possible weight.

Prim's algorithm
AQA, Edexcel, OCR

Use **Prim's algorithm** to find a minimum spanning tree of a network.

Step 1: Select any vertex as a starting point.

Step 2: Connect it to the vertex that will make an edge of minimum weight.

Step 3: Extend the tree by choosing an edge of smallest weight that joins with the previously selected edge(s).

Step 4: Repeat step 3 until all of the vertices are connected.

Decision Mathematics — Graphs and Networks

Example

Use Prim's algorithm to find a minimum spanning tree for the weighted graph shown.

Solution

Step 1: Select vertex A.

Step 2: The edge of minimum weight is AG. (1st edge)

Step 3: The edge of minimum weight that joins to AG is GC. (2nd edge)

Step 4: The edge of minimum weight connected to the existing tree AGC is GB. (3rd edge)

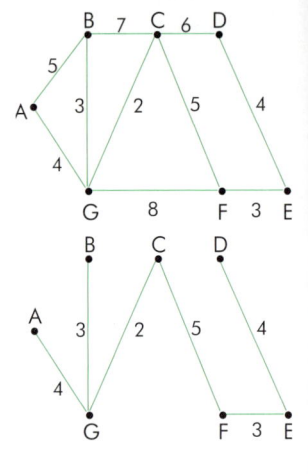

Extending the tree by choosing the edge of minimum weight connected to the existing tree AGBC is CF. (4th edge)

Likewise the fifth and sixth edges are FE and ED respectively.

Thus the weight of the minimum spanning tree is:

$4 + 3 + 2 + 5 + 3 + 4 = 21$

Kruskal's algorithm

AQA, Edexcel, OCR

Kruskal's algorithm is another method that you can use to find a minimum spanning tree.

Step 1: Choose an edge with minimum weight as the first subgraph.

Step 2: Extended the subgraph by choosing the next edge of minimum weight that will not complete a cycle.

Step 3: Repeat step 2 until all the vertices are connected.

Decision Mathematics — Graphs and Networks

Shortest path

AQA, Edexcel, OCR

The path covering the shortest distance between two vertices of a **network** is called the **shortest path**. It can be efficiently calculated by the use of **Dijkstra's algorithm**.

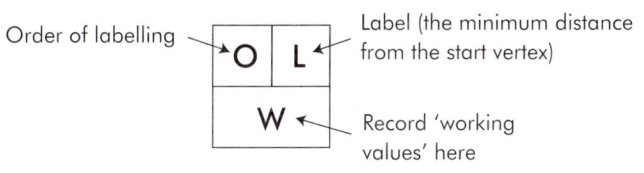

```
Order of labelling → | O | L | ← Label (the minimum distance
                     |   |   |    from the start vertex)
                     |   W   | ← Record 'working
                                  values' here
```

The steps in the algorithm rely on the above system of labelling for each vertex.

Step 1: Give the start vertex a label of 0 and order of labelling of 1.

Step 2: Enter the distance for each vertex directly connected to the one just labelled as a working value. Now, the vertex with the lowest working value becomes a label for that vertex and is given an order of labelling of 2.

Step 3: For each vertex directly connected to the one last given a label, add the edge distance to the label to obtain a total distance. This distance becomes the working value of the vertex unless a lower one has been found.

Step 4: Select the unlabelled vertex with the lowest working value and label it with that value.

Step 5: Repeat steps 3 and 4 until the target vertex is reached. The label value represents the shortest distance from the start vertex.

Step 6: To find the shortest path, trace the path back from the target vertex to the start vertex along the edges that satisfy:
length of edge = difference of labels

Decision Mathematics — Graphs and Networks

Example

Find the shortest distance from A to F and define the path taken.

Solution

Using Dijkstra's algorithm gives:

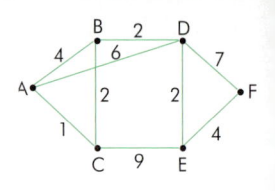

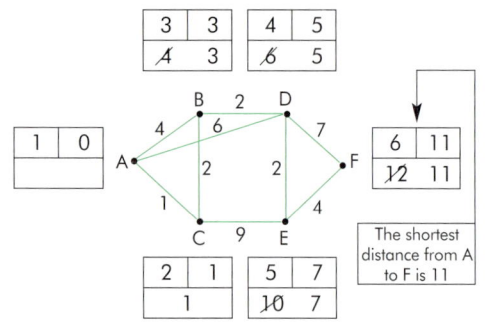

The shortest distance from A to F is 11.

Tracing the shortest path backwards using Step 6 gives FEDBA, thus the required path is ABDEF.

Travelling salesman problem

OCR

The travelling salesman problem involves finding a route of minimum length, passing through every vertex and returning to the start vertex. The optimal route may pass through some vertices more than once. No algorithm to date exists and so your work on this problem must be confined to finding an upper and lower bound to the solution.

Finding an upper bound

An upper bound is found by doubling the length of the minimum spanning tree. An improved (smaller) value can be found by looking for shortcuts back from the target vertex to the start vertex.

Finding a lower bound

Step 1: Erase a vertex along with any associated edges.

Step 2: Find a minimum spanning tree for the reduced diagram.

Step 3: Add the result from step 2 to the lengths of the two shortest edges.

Chinese postman problem

Edexcel, OCR

The Chinese postman problem involves finding a route of minimum length that covers every edge and returns to the start vertex.

A graph is **traversable** if every edge can be crossed but none more than once.

Graphs can be put into three categories to describe their traversability.

i All even vertices: The graph is traversable, starting and ending at the same vertex. Such a graph is called **Eulerian**.

ii Two odd vertices: The graph is traversable, starting at one odd vertex and ending at the other. Such a graph is called **semi-Eulerian**.

iii More than two odd vertices: The graph is not traversable. Such a graph is called **non-Eulerian**.

The **Chinese postman algorithm** can be **summarised** as follows.

Step 1: Identify all odd vertices.

Step 2: Arrange the odd vertices into different sets of two pairs.

Step 3: For each set, find a path of minimum length that joins each pair in that set. Hence, add these lengths to find the total minimum length for the chosen set.

Step 4: Choose the set that gives the lowest minimum length. Each pair in this set defines an edge which must be repeated in order to solve the problem.

Decision mathematics — Graphs and networks

Flows in networks
Edexcel

These are directed graphs that involve **flows** of liquids, gases or any other measurable quantities.

The edges may represent pipes, wires or roads that transport quantities from the **source** (a vertex having no incoming edges) to the **sink** (a vertex having no outgoing edges).

Each edge of the network has a **capacity** which represents the maximum allowable flow along that edge.

A **cut** divides the vertices into two sets, one containing the source and the other the sink.

The **capacity of a cut** is defined as the sum of the capacities of the edges that cross the cut, *taken in the direction from the source to the sink* (i.e. from the left side to the right side of the cut).

In the diagram, the capacity of cut_1 is $8 + 6 + 3 = 17$. The capacity of cut_2 is $2 + 3 = 5$.

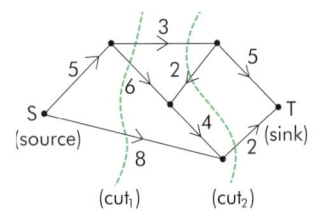

Note that for cut_2, the capacity of 2 is excluded as the flow is from the right side to the left side of the cut.

Minimum cut – maximum flow theorem
Edexcel

The **minimum cut – maximum flow** theorem states that the maximum level of flow through a network equals the capacity of the minimum cut.

Maximum flow = capacity of the minimum cut

DECISION MATHEMATICS — GRAPHS AND NETWORKS

There is no method for finding the minimum cut other than trial and error. Once this is calculated, you then need to allocate actual flows in each edge such that:

- the flow along each edge does not exceed its capacity
- at each vertex other than the source and the sink:

  total flow in = total flow out

- the total output from all source vertices is equal to the total input for all sink vertices.

Note: There is usually more than one possible route (i.e. pattern) for the maximum flow.

Flow augmentation

Edexcel

A flow augmentation algorithm is designed to build on a given flow through a network and can be applied repeatedly until an optimum outcome is reached.

Step 1: Give each edge an initial feasible flow, making sure that the flow is conserved at each vertex.

Step 2: Label the back and excess capacity for each edge.

Step 3: Search for a flow-augmenting path. If you can find one, then increase the flow along the path by the maximum feasible amount.

Step 4: Repeat steps 2 and 3 until the optimal flow has been found.

Decision Mathematics — Critical Path Analysis

Critical path

AQA, Edexcel

Critical path scheduling is a powerful technique that is widely used, for example, in the construction industry and in the installation of new equipment, as a means of **maximising** efficiency.

The **critical path** is the longest path (through the network) from start to termination and it determines the completion time of the entire project. The activities on this path are the **critical activities**. The **start vertex** is denoted by S and the **terminal vertex** by T.

Earliest starting time

The earliest starting time for an event A is the length of the **longest path** from S to A.

Latest starting time

The latest starting time for an event A is the **total time** for the project **less** the length of the **longest path** from A to T.

Float time

Float time = (latest start time) − (earliest start time)

Example

Determine the critical path for this network.
Hence by setting up a table, state which activities are critical.

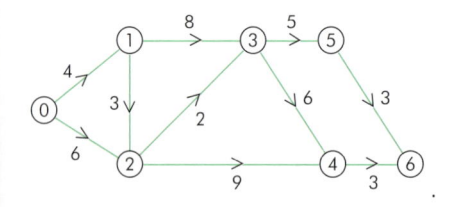

DECISION MATHEMATICS — CRITICAL PATH ANALYSIS

Solution

The critical path is the longest path through the network.

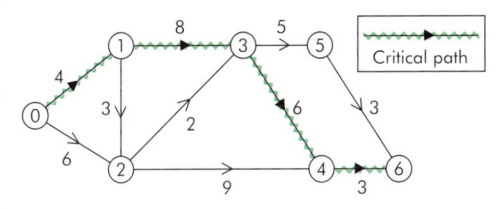

The critical path is $0 - 1 - 3 - 4 - 6$.

Critical activities are $A_{0,1}$, $A_{1,3}$, $A_{3,4}$ and $A_{4,6}$.

Event	Earliest start time (E)	Latest start time (L)	Float (L − E)
0	0	0	0*
1	4	4	0*
2	7	(21 − 12) 9	2
3	12	12	0*
4	18	18	0*
5	17	(21 − 3) 18	1
6	21	21	0*

Decision Mathematics — Linear Programming

Graphical method

AQA, Edexcel, OCR

Step 1: Identify the two **variables** in the problem.

Step 2: Express the given **constraints** in terms of the variables. Include non-negativity constraints i.e. $x \geq 0$, $y \geq 0$.

Step 3: Write the **objective function**, z, (i.e. the quantity to be **optimised**) in terms of the variables.

Step 4: Sketch the graph of each constraint.

Step 5: Shade out the *unwanted* region. The area that remains unshaded defines the **feasible region**.

Step 6: Find the coordinates of the **vertices** of the feasible region and calculate the value of z for each one. z will be **optimised** at one of these points.

Example

An office manager needs to buy filing cabinets from two suppliers. She has a maximum budget of £560, while the office has no more than 36 m² of floor space available. How many of each type of filing cabinet should she purchase, to maximise storage capacity?

Brand	Cost (£)	Capacity (m³)	Space required (m²)
Grange	40	4	3
Viking	80	6	4

Solution

Step 1: Let x = number of Grange cabinets and y = number of Viking cabinets. Summarise the information in a table.

Brand	Number of cabinets	Total cost	Space required	Capacity
Grange	x	$40x$	$3x$	$4x$
Viking	x	$80y$	$4y$	$6y$
Maximum available		≤ 560	≤ 36	To be **maximised**

Step 2: $40x + 80y \leq 560$
$3x + 4y \leq 36$
$x \geq 0, y \geq 0$

Step 3: Objective function: $z = 4x + 6y$

Steps 4 & 5:

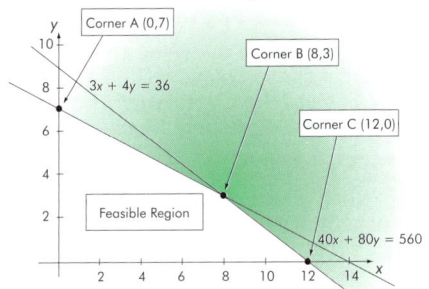

Corner A (0,7)
Corner B (8,3)
Corner C (12,0)
$3x + 4y = 36$
$40x + 80y = 560$
Feasible Region

Step 6: At $A\ (0, 7)$: $z = 4x + 6y = 0 + 42 = 42$
At $B\ (8, 3)$: $z = 4x + 6y = 32 + 18 = 50^*$
At $C\ (12, 0)$: $z = 4x + 6y = 48 + 0 = 48$ *Optimum

The manager should purchase 8 Grange and 3 Viking cabinets to **maximise** storage space.

Simplex algorithm
Edexcel, OCR

This approach for obtaining a linear programming solution uses a series of tableaux. The method systematically tests a number of feasible solutions until the final optimal solution is found. It is particularly useful when three or more variables are involved.

Step 1: Write the objective function to be maximised.

Step 2: Write the constraints in the form $ax + by + cz \leq k$. Also write the non-negativity constraints.

Step 3: Introduce **slack variables** to convert the constraints from inequalities: $ax + by + cz \leq k$ (from step 2) to equalities: $ax + by + cz + s_i = k$ where s_i for $i = 1, 2, ...$ are known as slack variables. Rearrange the objective function to the form $P - ax - by - cz = 0$.

DECISION MATHEMATICS — LINEAR PROGRAMMING

Step 4: Write the information in the **initial tableau**; include the objective function and the equalities formulated in step 3, with their corresponding **values**.

Step 5: Identify the **pivotal column** in your initial tableau. This is the one that contains the highest negative value.

Step 6: Divide each number in the **value** column by the number in the pivotal column, provided it is positive. The smallest of these results gives the **pivotal row**. The number that is in both the pivotal column and the pivotal row is the **pivot**.

Step 7: Divide each value in the pivotal row by the pivot.

Step 8: Turn the other values in the pivotal column to zero by adding or subtracting multiples of the pivotal row.

Step 9: If the objective row has no negative values, the **optimum tableau** has been found and the objective function maximised. If not, repeat steps 5–8 until this is achieved.

Example

Maximise the value of $P = x + 3y + 5z$ subject to:

$2x + 3y + z \leq 10 \qquad x + 4y + 3z \leq 18 \qquad x \geq 0, y \geq 0, z \geq 0$

Solution

Step 1: $P = x + 3y + 5z$

Step 2: $2x + 3y + z \leq 10,\ x + 4y + 3z \leq 18,\ x \geq 0, y \geq 0, z \geq 0$

Step 3: $2x + 3y + z + s_1 = 10 \qquad x + 4y + 3z + s_2 = 18$
$P - x - 3y - 5z = 0 \qquad$ *Objective function rearranged.*

Steps 4 & 5: Initial tableau:

Pivotal column ↓ (z)

	P	x	y	z	s_1	s_2	Value
objective function →	1	⁻1	⁻3	⁻5	0	0	0
	0	2	3	1	1	0	10
pivotal row →	0	1	4	**3**	0	1	18

↑ Pivot

DECISION MATHEMATICS   **LINEAR PROGRAMMING**

Step 6: i $\frac{10}{1} = 10$, $\frac{18}{3} = 6$

    ii The smaller of these results is 6 and we now taken this as our pivotal row.

    iii The pivot is 3 as it lies in both the pivotal column and the pivotal row.

Step 7:

Pivotal column

	P	x	y	z	s_1	s_2	Value
1st row →	1	−1	−3	−5	0	0	0
2nd row →	0	2	3	1	1	0	10
pivotal row →	0	$\frac{1}{3}$	$\frac{4}{3}$	**1**	0	$\frac{1}{3}$	6

↑ Pivot

Step 8:
- To turn the value in the first row of the pivotal column to zero we take: first row + 5 × pivotal row
- To turn the value in the second row of the pivotal column to zero we take: second row − pivotal row

first row + 5 × pivotal row ⟶

	P	x	y	z	s_1	s_2	Value
objective row →	1	$\frac{2}{3}$	$\frac{11}{3}$	0	0	$\frac{5}{3}$	30
	0	$\frac{5}{3}$	$\frac{5}{3}$	0	1	$-\frac{1}{3}$	4
	0	$\frac{1}{3}$	$\frac{4}{3}$	1	0	$\frac{1}{3}$	6

second row − pivotal row ⟶

Step 9: As the objective row has no negative values thus the optimum tableau has been reached.
It shows that the maximum value of P is 30 which occurs when $x = 0$, $y = 0$, $z = 6$, $s_1 = 4$ and $s_2 = 0$.

DECISION MATHEMATICS — MATCHINGS Edexcel

Matchings and graphs

A **bipartite graph** is a graph in which the vertices can be divided into two sets in such a way that no pair of vertices in the same set is connected by an edge.

A **matching** between two sets of a bipartite graph occurs when a pair of vertices is joined by at most one edge.

A **maximal matching** occurs when every vertex in one set is connected a vertex in the other set by at most one edge (refer to the diagram).

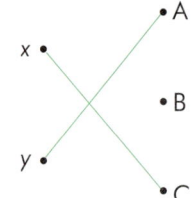

A **complete matching** occurs when every vertex in one set is connected to a vertex in the other set by at most one edge. This is only possible when the numbers of vertices in both sets are equal.

Matching improvement algorithm

This algorithm is used to increase the number of connections in a bipartite graph given an initial matching.

Step 1: Choose a vertex not connected in the initial matching and look for an **alternating path** to a vertex in the other set that is not connected.

Step 2: Each edge from step 1 that is part of the initial matching is deleted and each new edge is included.

Step 3: Repeat steps 1 and 2 until no more alternating paths can be found.

Note: In an alternating path, the edges alternate between those that are not in the initial matching and those that are.

Index

acceleration 47, 48–9, 50, 55
algebra 1–11, 25–31
algorithms 75–6
angle formulae 34–5, 36–7
area under a curve 23–4, 48
arithmetic series 13

bin packing 76
binary search 76
binomial expansion 27
binomial probability distribution 70–1
box and whisker plots 60
bubble sort 75

chain rule 39–40
Chinese postman problem 83
collisions 56–7
combinations 67
components 46
compound angle formulae 34–5
conditional probability 66
connected objects 55–6
continuous variables 72
coordinate geometry 12
correlation 73–4
cosecant 32
cosine 14, 16–18, 33
cotangent 32
critical path 86–7
cubics 7
cumulative distribution 61–3
curve sketching 7–9, 21, 28–31
quadratics 5, 11
trigonometric functions 14–18

data 58–63
differentiation 19–21, 39–41, 48
Dijkstra's algorithm 81–2
discrete variables 68–71
displacement 47, 48–9
distance 47, 48
domain 3–4, 25–6, 33
double angle formulae 34, 36–7

earliest event time 86, 87
equations
 of lines 12, 19
 of motion 47, 50
 solving 4–6, 10, 17–18, 35–8, 42–3
 see also functions
equilibrium 52, 53
exact ratios 16
expected value 68–9, 70
exponential functions 3, 28–9, 39, 40

factors 4, 10
feasible region 88, 89
flows 84–5
force 50–3, 55–6, 57
frequency distribution 61–3
friction 51, 52
functions 3–10, 25–31
 differentiating 19–21, 39–41
 expected value 69
 integrating 22–4, 40–1
 quadratic 4–6, 10, 11
 trigonometric 14–18, 32–8
 see also curve sketching

geometric distribution 71
geometric series 13
gradient 12, 47
graphs
 of motion 47–8
 and networks 77–85, 92
 and programming 88–9
 transformations 9, 15–16
 see also curve sketching
gravity 50

half-angle formulae 35, 36–7
histograms 61–3
hyperbolas 3, 8

identities 10, 17–18, 34–5
impulse 57
inclined plane 51
independent events 65
index laws 1
inequalities 11
integration 22–4, 40–1, 49
intercept 12
interquartile range 59, 61, 63
inverse functions 25–6
 trigonometric 33
iterative methods 42–3

Kruskal's algorithm 80

latest event time 86, 87

Index

lines 12, 19
   linear inequalities 11
logarithmic functions 30–1, 39, 40

mass 54, 55, 56–7
matchings 92
maxima 20, 21
mean 58, 63, 72
median 58, 60, 61, 63
midpoint 12
minima 20, 21
minimum cut – maximum flow theorem 84–5
mode 58, 63
modulus function 9, 26
moments 53
momentum 56–7
motion 47–8, 50, 52
mutually exclusive events 64

networks 77–87
normal (curves) 19
normal distribution 72, 73
normal reaction 51, 52
numerical methods 42–3

paths 77–9, 81–2
   critical path 86–7
periodic functions 14–15, 32
permutations 67
points of inflexion 20
Poisson distribution 71
polynomials 10, 27–8
Prim's algorithm 79–80
probability 64–7

probability distribution 68–72
programming 88–91
projectiles 50
Pythagoras' theorem 16
Pythagorean identities 34

quadratics 4–6, 10, 11
quartics 8
quick sort 75

radians 18
range (functions) 3–4, 25–6, 33
range (statistics) 58–9, 63
reaction 51, 52
regression 74
remainder theorem 28
resolving forces 51, 52, 53
resolving vectors 46
resultant force 51
resultant vectors 44

scalar multiplication 45–6
scalar quantities 44
scatter diagrams 73
secant 32
sequences 67
series 13
shuttle sort 75–6
simplex algorithm 89–91
simultaneous equations 10
sine 14, 16–18, 33
sketching *see* curve sketching

skew 59
speed 47, 48
spread 58–9, 60, 69
square roots 2, 4
standard deviation 59, 69, 72
stationary points 20–1
statistics 58–74
   diagrams in 60–3
stem plots 60–1
surds 2

tangent (tan) 15, 16–18, 33
tangent to a curve 19
tension 55–6
time 47–8, 86, 87
transformation method 38
transformations, graphical 9, 15–16
trapezium rule 43
travelling salesman problem 82–3
tree diagrams 65–6
trees (networks) 79–80
trigonometry 14–18, 32–8

variance 59, 69, 70
vectors 44–6, 49, 51
velocity 47, 48–9, 56–7
Venn diagrams 64–5
vertices 77–87, 92
   of quadratics 5, 6
volume of revolution 41

weight (force) 50, 51, 52
weight (networks) 79–80